MW00439200

The Best of the Bonnet

Also by Andrew Unger

Once Removed

THE BEST OF THE BONNET

by Andrew Unger

TURNSTONE PRESS

The Best of the Bonnet
copyright © Andrew Unger 2021
Micro Essays copyright © The Authors
Turnstone Press
Artspace Building
206-100 Arthur Street
Winnipeg, MB
R3B 1H3 Canada
www.TurnstonePress.com

All rights reserved. No part of this book may be reproduced or transmitted in any form or by any means—graphic, electronic or mechanical—without the prior written permission of the publisher. Any request to photocopy any part of this book shall be directed in writing to Access Copyright, Toronto.

Turnstone Press gratefully acknowledges the assistance of the Canada Council for the Arts, the Manitoba Arts Council, the Government of Canada through the Canada Book Fund, and the Province of Manitoba through the Book Publishing Tax Credit and the Book Publisher Marketing Assistance Program.

Cover image: Daily Bonnet Logo by Jackson Friesen.

Printed and bound in Canada by Friesens.

Library and Archives Canada Cataloguing in Publication

Title: The best of the Bonnet / Andrew Unger.
Names: Unger, Andrew, 1979- author. | Unger, Andrew, 1979- Daily bonnet.
Identifiers: Canadiana (print) 20210358130 | Canadiana (ebook)
    20210358475 | ISBN 9780888017390 (softcover) | ISBN 9780888017406
    (EPUB) | ISBN 9780888017413 (PDF)
Subjects: LCSH: Mennonites—Humor.
Classification: LCC PS8641.N44 O53 2021 | DDC C814/.6—dc23

MANITOBA ARTS COUNCIL
CONSEIL DES ARTS DU MANITOBA

Canada Council   Conseil des arts
for the Arts   du Canada

Contents

DOAGES'BEREJCHT (A DAILY REPORT)

BROODASCHAUFT (A CHURCH MEETING)

FE'SCHLUCKE (WHEN FOOD OR DRINK GOES DOWN THE WRONG TUBE)

WELTLIJCHTJEIT (WORLDLINESS)

FREIWILLIGES (THE TALK)

WEADABUAK ENN SOO WIEDA (WORD BOOK ETC.)

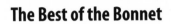
The Best of the Bonnet

Despite having the appearance of news articles, the writings contained herein are entirely works of fiction. To misquote the Apostle, "they have the form of news, while denying its power." This isn't to say that these articles are lies, per se, as that would imply some intention to deceive, whereas the intention here is to entertain, to provoke, maybe even to cause one to *fe'schlucke* on occasion (please be careful). Likewise, do not fret about the use of names. You might read about a Mr. Friesen of Altona, for example, but rest assured, this is not the same Mr. Friesen of Altona that you know. This is a fictional Mr. Friesen of Altona. Furthermore, anything said about a public figure (for example, Menno Simons) should not be compared to the historic record, as you are likely to find considerable deviation from fact.

"Lies! Lies! All lies! This is obviously written by someone who knows nothing about Mennonites and just wants to make them look bad."

—Correspondence from a satisfied reader

The Story of Kjnels P. Baerg, Founder of *The Daily Bonnet*

On a hot summer day in 1905, Kjnels P. Baerg, just 18 at the time, was baptized on the banks of the beautiful Molotschna River in South Russia. Church records are unclear whether he undertook this baptism upon confession of his faith or simply to avoid undue scrutiny from the elders, but we do know that as soon as he came up out of the water, he was greeted by a very eager Loewen couple who urged him to join them and their eight very eligible daughters for *faspa* that afternoon to discuss his "prospects." As a freshly baptized young Mennonite man, everyone expected him to choose a life partner by the end of the afternoon. It didn't matter that he owned no land and spent his days observing the locals and scribbling in his journal. Well, it did matter to some, actually, which is why only the Loewens of Rosendorf were willing to marry a lazy, good-for-nothing *fülenza* like Kjnels P. Baerg, a man who was well known in the community for his scandalous interest in books rather than livestock.

However, Baerg was a man with a mission—some say it came from above—and that mission did not involve procreating with a Loewen, or even a Driedger or Plett for that matter. And so, while his pants were still wet, he hitched up his wagon and headed for the city, where he boarded a train north and then a boat and then another boat and a few more too, and finally made his way to the New World. Surprisingly, his early journals, which are filled with minutiae such as lists of every Hermann Sudermann book he read and all the ways in which the pastor had erred in his latest sermon, contain large gaps of unaccounted-for time during this period of travel, and historians suspect the reason for this lack of detail was that young Baerg must have spent his very last ruble buying a boat ticket and a Kroeger clock and that nothing was left for ink and paper. Either that or the pages went missing during the great *Kleine Gemeinde* fire of 1912. We do know, however, that he arrived in Canada in the late fall of 1905 and that he was alone.

Since Kjnels did not settle on the Canadian Prairies during one of the major Mennonite migrations of the 1870s or 1920s, he was considered a bit of an outsider. Some say he was the first in southern Manitoba to be labelled a *Russländer* or "Russian." The term was used as a slur, albeit a mild one, and like all slurs, it really didn't make a whole lot of sense. After all, the others had come from Russia too, just a few decades earlier, and most of them were no more distantly related than second cousins. Labelling one group as distinct from the other seems, to our contemporary eyes, unnecessarily pedantic. Nevertheless, because he was a *Russländer*, and the first one at that, he had trouble finding work in Manitoba. He tried to get a job in Hochfeld as a cheesemaker but was turned down since he clearly had a Molotschna accent. He said *kok* when he should have said *küak*, and *bok* when he should have said *büak*. He spent a few months in Rosenort, but all he could do was *schekjbenjel* work and there, too, he found Loewens who were far too eager to wed. Finally, he wound up on the other side of the river in Kuchenhof, a village that no longer exists today after the entire community left Canada for Mexico to avoid the sweet and sinful temptation of Rogers Golden Syrup. It was there in Kuchenhof that he purchased a printing press from a recently defunct gospel leaflet printer, and it was there, in an old cowshed in Kuchenhof, that Kjnels P. Baerg created the world's first Plautdietsch newspaper, *Dee Däajlijch Düak*.

Dee Däajlijch Düak quickly became the most widely circulated publication ever founded by a *schekjbenjel*, and it wasn't long before Baerg hired a stable of foreign correspondents and expanded his reach to include coverage of Mennonite happenings in far-flung places like La Crete and Yarrow and Goessel. The fact that the publication was in Plautdietsch, an unwritten language at the time, meant he could spell words however he wished. Many folks, Mennonites included, struggled to decipher his cryptic texts until 1941 when Baerg published the first-ever Plautdietsch dictionary. Sadly, the book was quickly confiscated by Canadian authorities who viewed the language as too close to German and deemed it a threat to national security. When Baerg's printing press was attacked by an angry mob of Englishers in June 1943, he was forced to print his articles in grammatically unstable English for the remainder of the war. These were dark times for Baerg.

After the Second World War, however, the paper flourished and peaked at 606 subscribers in 1965. This postwar success was due in part to Baerg's commitment to investigative journalism, such as his award-winning coverage of the Kroeker Missle Crisis. While the occasional article ruffled some feathers, for the most part, people appreciated the window to the world (or at least the world of Friesens, Koops, and Klassens) that his paper provided. Still, he was the first Mennonite writer to be accused of "airing our dirty aprons in public," an accusation that Baerg dismissed by noting that "if one did not want such items on display, then one should take more care not to dirty one's aprons." The newspaper was published from 1911 until Baerg's death in 1976. He is buried in a farmer's field near the former site of Kuchenhof, though the precise location is unknown.

For decades after the publication's demise, extant copies of *Dee Däajlijch Düak* were hard to come by, with collectable issues, such as the first appearance of Wunda Frü, reaching record prices in the "Something Special" display cases at local MCC thrift stores. Until recently, no copies of *Dee Däajlijch Düak* Vol. 1 No. 1 were known to exist. Even many of the later issues had been reduced to scraps found in the walls of demolished southern Manitoba homes.

In 2007, however, everything changed thanks to the estate of Mrs. Helen Klippenstein of Blumenhimmel, a meticulous clipper of articles. The Klippenstein Clippings, as they are known by scholars, filled dozens of scrapbooks and contained articles from nearly every year that *Dee Däajlijch Düak* was in print. The collection was bequeathed to Klippenstein's great-nephew and floundering writer Andrew Unger with the appropriately utilitarian, albeit vague, instructions to "put these to good use." It was the largest inheritance ever passed on to an Unger.

After spending nearly a decade devouring everything the scrapbooks would reveal, Unger found that he shared his ancestor's penchant for writing and for being a *fülenza* and all of that. Plus, he needed extra cash to pay for his annual trip to Chihuahua to visit the *frindschauft*. So when Unger discovered that the publication rights to Baerg's writings were in limbo and that the rest of the family had no interest in the project, he seized the opportunity to revive the gazette. Forty years after the famed paper ceased publication and just months after local church elders lifted the ban on Internet usage, *Dee Däajlijch Düak* saw new life as an online English-language publication and thus the legacy of Kjnels P. Baerg continues to this day.

A word on the title. *Dee Däajlijch Düak* literally means "The Daily Kerchief, Shawl, or Head Covering," but Unger felt *The Daily Bonnet*, while not a direct translation, was more succinct and had a better ring to it. The English name was also thought to have more commercial potential, since marketing experts have shown time and again that viability, in the lucrative North American market at least, has a direct negative correlation to the number of umlauts in a title.

One final note: during his five years at the helm of the publication, some readers have perceived in Unger's work a certain element of drollness. Out of context, Unger notes, one might even consider these articles "funny." However, the author hopes that the perceived levity found in this collection will not detract from its cultural importance and trusts that readers will "treat these articles with the reverence and respect that they deserve as documentation of the lives of real people."

DOAGES'BEREJCHT

(A DAILY REPORT)

Friesen-Friesen Wedding Is Well Attended by Local Friesens

STEINBACH, MB

Hundreds of Friesens from across southeastern Manitoba descended on the local EMBC church this past Saturday to attend the wedding of James Friesen and Anna Friesen (no relation).

"I was so excited to see Friesen marry Friesen (no relation)," said Mrs. Friesen of Grunthal. "I just know those two Friesens are meant for each other."

Friesen, 25, proposed to Friesen (no relation), 24, at the Friesen farm this past spring, and the couple immediately began planning the Friesen-Friesen wedding.

"The usher asked whether I wanted to sit on the Friesen or the Friesen (no relation) side," said Mr. Friesen (no relation to the aforementioned Mrs. Friesen). "I don't know how the usher couldn't tell just by looking at me that I was a Friesen (no relation). I mean, it's obvious. I have the Friesen (no relation) nose."

The seating confusion came after the Friesen side of the church seemed to fill up quickly. After a while, the ushers discreetly sat some Friesens on the Friesen (no relation) side just to even things out a bit.

"Eventually the Friesens (no relation) and Friesens were all mixed up," said usher Joshua Friesen. "Well, I guess it's okay that the Friesens got to know each other."

The bride announced that after the wedding, she would be known as Anna Friesen-Friesen (no relation), although more conservative relatives have wondered why she couldn't have just taken her husband's name.

Children Walk In on Parents Having Meddachschlop
BOW ISLAND, AB

Mr. and Mrs. Loewen were enjoying a pleasant Sunday afternoon *meddachschlop* this weekend when their young children, Ethan and Brittany, were startled by peculiar sounds that required their immediate investigation.

"*Rüt met die!* Get out of here right now!" exclaimed Mr. Loewen, as the children pushed open their parents' door without knocking. "Can't you see your mom and I are busy having a peaceful afternoon nap?"

The children ran back to the living room in a panic, quickly followed by Mr. Loewen in a housecoat who turned up the volume on the *Veggie Tales* video to maximum.

"When your mother and I are having *meddachschlop* I expect the volume to stay like this," said Mr. Loewen sternly. "And we are not to be disturbed!"

After that embarrassing moment, Mr. and Mrs. Loewen vowed to be much more discreet with their *meddachschlop* and are determined to take the necessary precautions to avoid such an outcome again.

"Dennis needs to *meddachschlop* a whole lot quieter," said Mrs. Loewen. "Meanwhile, I'll be sure to lock the door and crank up the Gaither quartet."

Mennonite Golfer Spends 3 Hours Looking for Lost Ball

GIROUX, MB

Area man Robert Wall, 62, created a three-hour delay looking for a lost ball during his afternoon golf match this past Tuesday. Wall, who is an avid golf ball finder, was less concerned about the lost stroke than about the high cost of golf balls.

"I bring one ball with me and that is it yet," said Wall, traipsing through the bush. "I've been playing with this same yellowed and cracked Titleist for years."

Wall says he's able to identify his ball because it has a Loewen Windows logo on it. He originally found the ball in the water hazard at the Steinbach Fly-In course back in 1998.

"Some other groups wanted to play through," said Wall, "but they can wait. I'm not sure why everyone has to be in such a hurry. Think of all the money you could save if every time you hit a crooked shot you spent an hour or two recovering the ball."

Wall is also known to reuse broken tees and sneak his own beverages onto the course. He says he used to play with some fellow retirees, but now golfs alone because his friends just couldn't keep up with his pace.

"It usually takes me about 10 hours to play nine holes," said Wall. "I don't think my buddies have that kind of stamina. Plus, they're never prepared like I am with waist-high waders in case I plunk one into the water hazard."

Mennonite Woman Buys Back Her Own Clothes at the MCC Store

ALTONA, MB

Mrs. Erin Stobbe, 38, of Altona donated then bought back dozens of blouses, skirts, and denim products from the local MCC Thrift Shop this month. She says the buybacks were not intentional, but "just happen sometimes" when one purchases the volume of secondhand clothes that she does.

"The other day I was at the Altona MCC and found this great pair of black skinny jeans … and they fit like a glove. I just had to snatch them up before some other size 28 came along and snagged them!" said Stobbe. "But when I tried them on at home in front of the full-length mirror I thought, 'Well, Erin, these look awfully familiar.'"

Stobbe donates two full garbage bags of clothes to the MCC each week, but always makes sure to purchase just as much in return.

"I think of it as a rental shop without any late fees," said Stobbe. "I knew my old American Apparel gabardine tennis skirt wouldn't last long, so as soon as I saw it on the shelf, I bought it right back!"

Stobbe can be seen shopping at the Altona MCC between 11:00 a.m. and 2:00 p.m. on Saturdays and donating everything back on Thursdays during her lunch break.

Mennonite Man Drives Really Slow
'To Be a Witness for the Lord'
SASKATOON, SK

Traffic was backed up for miles in Saskatoon this past Friday as Matthias Neufeld, 74, of Dalmeny decided to go to the city and drive really slow during rush hour.

"This is my mission field," explained Neufeld. "We are to flee from sin and worldliness, and what better way to show the world the love of God than by driving 20 or 30 kilometres below the speed limit?"

Car horns blared and commuters rolled down their windows to yell at the Mennonite man, but he remained firm in his resolve to traverse Idylwyld Drive in such a manner that would please the Lord.

"They were just upset because the Devil's got a hold of them," said Neufeld. "The more they honked and yelled, the more I maintained my steadfast commitment to show them the way of truth and light."

Neufeld also flirted with the idea of driving the wrong way down the freeway, but decided he had done enough witnessing for the day and took the Yellowhead back to Dalmeny where his wife, Martha, eagerly awaited the very delayed arrival of her missionary husband.

"He is a hero," she said, handing him a *schnetje* lovingly coated with strawberry-rhubarb jam. "When the roll is called up yonder, there will be many a jewel in his crown for all the good work he's doing reaching unsaved drivers."

Rapture Occurs Just Before Newlyweds Have a Chance to Consummate Their Marriage

CHILLIWACK, BC

Every chaste young man's biggest fear came true last night as Eric Dueck and Sarah Barkman were miraculously raptured just moments before they were able to consummate their marriage.

"I just knew this would happen," said 21-year-old Eric, who had been eagerly anticipating his wedding night ever since he first heard about this thing called "sex" from Pastor Dave during premarital counselling.

The rapture took place just after the reception in the MB church basement. According to traditional Anabaptist doctrine, the Bible clearly teaches that in Heaven people will "neither marry nor be given in marriage, but instead they will be like angels."

"Yeah … and angels don't have sex," said a disappointed Eric from his heavenly perch. "It's true that I didn't know much about it, but I would have at least liked to have been given the chance to learn."

His new wife Sarah, however, was not as concerned about the situation as her earthly husband.

"I have to admit, for me it was a relief," said Sarah. "That was the one thing about marrying Eric that I was a little nervous about, but now I don't have to worry. I'm just glad my floral arrangements turned out the way I planned."

Eric says he's glad to be in Heaven but wishes he and Sarah had snuck off to the Travelodge sometime between the ceremony and the reception.

"Ugh. We had like three hours and all we were doing was taking photographs," said Eric. "We really should have had our priorities straight."

How to Win at the Mennonite Game: A Comprehensive Guide

The Mennonite Game is easy to play but difficult to master, especially since Mennonites have been playing the game for decades without a clear set of rules. Using the following points system, a clear winner can be determined. Simply tally up your score throughout your lifetime and have your total engraved on your tombstone for future Mennonites to see. This game is appropriate for all ages, and although younger people may have more energy to tally points, older Mennonites certainly have the advantage when it comes to knowledge about aunts and uncles and second cousins.

- Any time you are asked "Who is your father?" or "Who is your mother?"—5 points
- Any time you ask someone else these same questions —5 points
- If you can ask and answer in Plautdietsch—20 points
- If the asker ruffles up your hair or pinches your cheek while asking—10 points
- If you ask someone who they are related to and it turns out they aren't Mennonite—minus 5 points
- Any time you are asked by a stranger which church you go to—10 points
- If you name some local Mennonite church in response—20 points
- If you're lying when you say it—minus 5 points
- If you only attend church for Christmas and Easter—5 points
- If you used to attend but don't anymore—2 points

- If you've been completely turned off by church because of how you were treated in the past and spend an hour or two regaling the asker with tales of this mistreatment—minus 50 points
- Owning a family history book—5 points per book
- Politely smiling and thanking your Uncle Gerhard for the spiral-bound self-published history book—15 points
- Actually reading the darn thing—50 points
- Tracing at least one line of ancestors back to Russia, Germany, or Prussia—5 points
- Tracing at least one line of ancestors back to The Netherlands, Belgium, or Switzerland—10 points
- Discovering a non-Mennonite in your family tree—minus 10 points
- Discovering a famous Mennonite in your family tree (like misguided adventurer Claas Epp Jr. or famed Nebraska sheep rancher Peter Jansen)—20 points
- Discovering a relation to Menno Simons—100 points
- Visiting an important Mennonite historic site—20 points
- Defacing it—minus 50 points
- If you can name all your cousins including the really young ones—10 points
- If you can name at least one second cousin—10 points
- Marrying a first cousin—50 points
- Marrying a second cousin—40 points
- Marrying a third cousin—30 points
- Marrying a fourth cousin or higher—20 points
- Marrying a first cousin once removed—40 points

- Marrying a second cousin once removed—30 points
- Marrying a third cousin once removed—20 points
- Marrying anyone else in the *Loewen Book*—10 points
- Divorcing any of the aforementioned people—minus 10 points
- Having relatives on both sides of the Red River—5 points
- Each time you cross the river to visit them—2 points per trip
- Having relatives who still live in the old country—20 points
- If your middle name is your mother's maiden name—20 points
- If you know what Grandma's Window is without having to Google it—20 points
- If you actually have a subscription to it—40 points
- Routinely referring to your relatives as *"frindschauft"*—20 points
- If you understand that the Mennonites are a religious denomination and not actually an ethnicity—1,000 points

Mennonite Lingerie Now Available at Aganetha's Secret
ROSENORT, MB

Rosenort is abuzz with excitement this week for the grand opening of a new store that specializes in the finest Mennonite lingerie. Started by local undergarment enthusiast Mrs. Aganetha Siemens, 72, the new store features intimate items for the discerning Mennonite woman.

"Just imagine whatever your grandmother wore and we've got it," said Mrs. Siemens. "We're bringing back bloomers, girdles, and corsets, in addition to our extensive line of slips designed specifically to hang just a little longer than your hemline."

Siemens says her store offers a wide selection of wholesome alternatives for shoppers who may find the lingerie at the city stores "a little too sexy."

"Women always ask their husbands to stay in the car when they go to those city stores," said Siemens. "That's understandable, but at Aganetha's Secret, there's nothing to worry about as we've got a little coffee shop where the men can sit and *spezeare* while their wives are trying on a pair of thick brown nylons. Not to mention that the raciest image we have on our walls is a floor-to-ceiling ad of Oma Plett in a modest nightie."

Mrs. Siemens is proud of her selection of products but says that customer service is really what sets her undergarment store apart from the rest.

"I'll even take the time to help you roll down your pantyhose to the ankles and match your nylons with the perfect pair of white sneakers," said Siemens, removing a curler from her hair. "With my fabulous selection and unbeatable service, I'm confident that Aganetha's Secret won't be a secret for long!"

Thousands of Mennonites Set Up Lawn Chairs Just Outside Concert Gates to Avoid Paying

NIVERVILLE, MB

Always trying to get something for nothing, tens of thousands of Mennonites are pitching their lawn chairs just outside the fence at the annual country music festival in downtown Niverville this weekend.

"Yeah, well, I can hear perfectly fine from over on Ash Grove Crescent," said frugal country music enthusiast Wanda Doerksen, 55, who missed her chance to get a prime spot right behind the fence with the Elias family. "I'm okay over here, though. Why should I pay $25 so that the concert breaks even and the artist gets paid when I can faintly hear it all for free just five or six blocks away?"

While the town has parked huge semi-trailers all along the concert fencing to block the view from non-paying citizens, locals, it seems, are content to hear the music from a distance.

"I've heard all my favourite country artists this way," explained Doerksen. "Last year I plopped myself down just behind the Maple Leaf Agri-Farms building and, let me tell you, the pedal steel guitar never sounded better. In my opinion, though, the best seats in the house are just behind the Chicken Chef, but good luck scoring that spot. Not that I'm buying any fried chicken. I've brought along plenty of *knackzoat.*"

Doerksen recently purchased a lovely new set of foldable lawn chairs with Canadian flags on the back, which she and her husband, Dan, plan to haul around on the free concert circuit throughout the summer.

Mennonite Man Storms Out of Jazz Club, Claims 'Far Too Much Sax'

YARROW, BC

Local man Peter Harder, 67, was so disgusted with a jazz performance in Vancouver this past weekend that he stood up right in the middle of "St. Thomas" and stormed out in a huff. Harder had never heard jazz music before and claimed he "didn't know there would be so much sax."

"I'm pretty sure this was what Pastor Jim was preaching against just last week," said Harder. "I walked in to see a man on the stage doing solo sax ... then a woman joined him. It was pornographic!"

Harder was encouraged to attend the event by his daughter Amber, who had hoped to expose her father to a few new cultural experiences.

"I didn't think there would be so much explicit sax," said Harder. "As soon as they announced the next song contained a trio, I was out of there!"

Harder was equally disgusted by flyers left on all the seats that advertised "private sax lessons."

"There's nothing they can teach me that my Betty and I don't already know," said Harder, "and I certainly don't need some beatnik in a turtleneck teaching me about sax!"

Harder is very disappointed that his daughter dragged him to such an event as he was really hoping she would be saving sax for marriage.

Divorced Mennonites Remain Cousins, Legal Expert Says
HARRISONBURG, VA

Settling an age-old question that has baffled legal scholars for centuries, renowned barrister and American law expert Rosanna L. Weaver of Harrisonburg claims there's no longer any room for debate when it comes to Mennonite divorce.

"They remain cousins," said Weaver. "Even in cases of desertion or adultery, the divorced Mennonite couple simply reverts to the status they had before they were lawfully wed, that of first or second cousins."

While this scenario has not been tested in court for quite some time, Weaver believes that there is clear precedent in this matter, and that any legal challenge to the cousin status of divorced Mennonites would fail in a court of law.

"I refer you to the case of Smucker versus Commonwealth of Pennsylvania," said Weaver. "The judge ruled that both Mr. and Mrs. Smucker would remain Smuckers even after their divorce, and that they could and should continue to attend Smucker gatherings regardless of their marital status."

Mennonite leaders were delighted to learn this new information, which they believe will be well received not just by Smuckers, but by Shenks and Wengers too.

"It's comforting to know," said one Mennonite elder, "that for better or for worse, for richer or for poorer, in sickness and in health, Mennonite couples will remain cousins forever."

Harry Dyck Considers Name Change

KLEEFELD, MB

After years on the farm without a care in the world, newly retired dairy farmer Mr. Harry A. Dyck of the Kleefeld area is now seriously considering a name change.

"My friends are giving me mixed advice on this one," said Dyck from his room at the local manor. "Some say, '*Oba*, Harry, it's a good name yet,' while others say, '*Na*, Harry, I think it's time for a change once.'"

Dyck says now that he's retired, he has a lot of time to think and is concerned that his name gives the wrong impression.

"You meet a lot of new people when you move onto the second floor of the Greenhaven Seniors' Home, and they all want to know your name," said Dyck. "People have certain expectations of you when you've got a name like this … I'm not sure if I can live up to them."

Dyck has reportedly asked all the nurses to call him "Harold" until he can come up with a suitable alternative.

"They're very professional," said Dyck. "They just go about their business as if my name was Richard Harder or Peter Friesen or anything else."

Greenhaven nurse Amanda Brown says she treats Dyck just like any other client.

"To be honest, this is not the first Harry Dyck I've encountered," said Brown. "We have a new one every few years. Harry Dycks come and go. I'm used to it."

Mr. Dyck plans to make a final decision sometime this week before the Singles Meet 'n Greet next Tuesday afternoon.

Mennonite Woman Recalls Traumatic Near-Dance Experience
DALMENY, SK

Area woman and budding writer Bertha Froese, 74, has published a new memoir titled *Dancing is for Real* which recounts her horrific near-dance experience in the summer of 2012.

"There I was at my cousin's wedding yet," said Bertha. "I was sitting at the table. I think there was some music playing. All I know is it sure wasn't any hymn I had heard before. Well, then this handsome man in grey slacks came up to me and asked me if I'd like to join him. I said sure. I had no idea what was going to happen. Well, the next thing I knew he was twirling and whirling me around all over the room. It was truly awful."

After years of reflection, Bertha is only now coming to terms with what happened to her on that fateful night.

"I danced," said Bertha. "I know that some people don't believe in dancing, but I can tell you it's very real. I know this because for a few minutes I was there ... dancing."

Bertha's new book is intended to warn people and get them to think seriously about what their futures might hold and whether those futures will include dancing or not.

"I pray that my book will be a blessing to all those Mennonites out there who have doubts about their non-dancing faith," said Bertha. "Dancing is most definitely for real ... and it's absolutely horrific."

Renowned Mennonite Scholar Unable to Locate Car in Parking Lot

FRESNO, CA

World-renowned expert on the Anabaptist exegesis of the Synoptic Gospels, Dr. Dirk W. Thiessen is always able to find minute errors in the Works Cited pages of undergraduate papers but was totally unable to locate his own car in the university parking lot on Thursday.

"Some students confuse APA and MLA formatting," explained Thiessen as he walked up and down the rows of cars in a feeble attempt to locate his vehicle. "They put the commas in the wrong places, they put two spaces instead of one, they put the city before the publisher and so on … Hey, where the heck is my Prius?"

Thiessen wandered the Fresno Pacific University parking lot for a good hour, frantically clicking the button on his key fob, hoping he was close enough to the car that the horn would honk.

"This happens every day," explained Thiessen. "I get here at nine, go to class, give a lecture, mark some papers, and by the end of the day my head is so full of the political theology of A. James Reimer as it relates to Paul Tillich that I just can't for the life of me remember where I parked the Toyota."

The sun was already setting by the time Thiessen reluctantly recruited a graduate student to help locate his car. The student quickly pointed out that Thiessen wasn't even in the right lot.

"Ugh, typical grad student," said Thiessen. "Thinks that just because he read two books on Bonhoeffer last semester he knows everything."

Students wishing to consult with Dr. Thiessen have been informed that his office hours have been dramatically reduced this semester to give the learned fellow all the time he needs to find his car.

Dutch Blitz Tournament Results in Hundreds of Casualties

LANCASTER, PA

More than three hundred serious injuries and five fatalities were reported at this year's Lancaster Seniors' Dutch Blitz tournament. The card game, which requires four players to simultaneously throw down cards at a furious pace, is popular with Mennonites despite the chronic injuries.

"This is just as we expected. Every year it's like this," said event organizer and three-time Dutch Blitz champion Jacob Gladfelter. "With all that frantic energy and hand slapping, people are bound to get injured."

Gladfelter says he is now retired from competitive Dutch Blitzing after a twisted wrist and broken thumb sidelined him during the 2003 season.

"It's a rough game," explained Gladfelter. "We do everything we can to prevent injuries, but when you play Dutch Blitz, you have to accept certain risks ... and permanent bodily disfigurement is just one of them."

Dutch Blitz has been popular among the historic peace churches for decades and, for many, it's the only acceptable method of releasing some pent-up frustration.

"Around here, Dutch Blitz is a blood sport," said Gladfelter. "It's too bad that some people get hurt, but given that Dutch Blitz is the only non-sinful card game, I guess we'll just have to put up with a significant likelihood of injury."

If current rates persist, Pennsylvania will have lost more than 40 percent of its population due to Dutch Blitz injuries within the next five years.

Massive Miriam Toews Statue to Be Erected in Steinbach
STEINBACH, MB

More than a decade after her best-selling novel *A Complicated Kindness* ruthlessly skewered her hometown of Steinbach, a 100-metre-high statue of Miriam Toews is set for construction on the corner of Main and Brandt.

"All is forgiven, Miriam," said local woman Susanna Giesbrecht, who spearheaded the statue campaign. "We felt it was time we honoured Steinbach's most famous former resident, even if you didn't really like it here and left as soon as you could."

It is hoped that the statue, which is estimated to cost between $80 million and $100 million, will attract tourists from across the Rural Municipality of Hanover and maybe even from as far away as Rosenort. The cost of construction will be offset by a small increase in library fees.

"Borrowing books will now cost a nominal $40 to $50, depending on if it's a chapter book or not," said Giesbrecht. "I think readers will also be excited to know that, for the first time ever, we're allowing folks to sign out Miriam Toews's books, although not the ones that make Steinbach look bad."

The statue, when completed, will be among the tallest free-standing structures in the world when measured from its base to the top of the airship docking station.

"See, that Jesus statue they've got down there in Rio, it's up on a hill," explained Steinbach city councillor Cornelius B. Reimer. "As you know, Steinbach is flat, so the thing's gotta be tall. Besides, we've gotta be able to see it above the Credit Union building."

At press time, Miriam Toews could not be reached for comment, as she was a long, long, long way from Steinbach.

Mennonite Woman Dies, Donates Her Organs
CHORTITZ, SK

L ocal woman Mrs. Mildred Fast passed away peacefully in her sleep this past Sunday at the age of 96. Thankfully, she signed her organ donor card and her wide selection of electric home organs have gone to those who need them.

"Mennonite churches are begging people to sign their organ donor cards," said Mrs. Florence Wiens, head of the Chortitz Mennonite Church Organ Procurement department. "You're not going to need your organs when you die, so if they're still in working condition, we'd love to have them."

It's estimated that Mrs. Fast's organs saved more than a dozen evening hymn sings.

"Considering their age, her Wurlitzers were in remarkable shape," said Mrs. Wiens. "I bet Mrs. Fast would be delighted to see her organs playing the Doxology in churches across Saskatchewan."

Mrs. Wiens hopes that Mrs. Fast's generosity will be noted by others with gently used organs.

"It's always sad when a loved one passes away, but it's nice to see that her organs did not go to waste," said Mrs. Wiens. "I urge everyone to sign their organ donor card. They don't even have to be Hammonds. We'll take any organs in working condition."

Mrs. Wiens assures concerned donors that if you entrust your organs to her, they will never ever be used to play rock songs.

20-Year-Old Spinster Gives Up on Marriage
STEINBACH, MB

After two full years working the till at Penner Foods and a steady stream of boyfriends who didn't propose, local spinster Rosemary B. Ratzlaff, who turns 20 this month, says she has given up hope of ever finding a life partner.

"At my age it's too late, because everyone at Penner's is already paired up," said Ratzlaff. "Plus, when you're 20 you start to see the ravages of age and the boys don't look at you anymore. I might as well pack my bags and go live with my great-aunt Edna at Mennohome Manor."

In preparation for a marriage proposal, Ratzlaff was recently baptized, but alas, Thomas Wall fell for Angela Esau at the parcel pickup training session this spring, leaving Ratzlaff the lone unmarried employee.

"Well, I guess all this time bagging groceries was a total waste!" exclaimed the visibly upset young woman.

As an unmarried Mennonite woman, Ratzlaff has been given the choice of either going into nursing or spending a few decades as a foreign missionary.

"I always thought I'd become a photographer ... or maybe try to get into the engineering program at the U of M," she said, "but since I'm still not married, I guess it's Burkina Faso for me."

It is estimated that the romantic relationships established at Penner Foods over the decades have resulted in more than 100,000 children, who will be packing AD Penner Park this summer for the 60th annual reunion picnic. At press time, Rosemary B. Ratzlaff is still looking for a date for the event.

How to Talk to Your Children About Sex: A Guide for Mennonite Parents

Talking to your children about the birds and bees can be an uncomfortable scenario for Mennonite parents, many of whom just send the kids off to school and cross their fingers that they'll figure it all out somehow. While that may have worked for older generations, the kids of today require a more direct approach. *The Daily Bonnet* has consulted with pastors, Sunday school teachers, farmhands, and other experts in the field to create this sex education guide for Mennonite parents. We hope you, and your children, will find it more than a little helpful.

1. Refer to all body parts by their proper Plautdietsch name. Talking about sex is not easy for Mennonites, so go ahead and revert to your mother tongue. Here are some words for body parts that may come in handy: *hinjarenj, bossem, lenj, footjelentj*. Make it very clear that none of these parts are to be used, touched, or seen at any time.

2. Wait until your children are the right age: 40. You don't want to scar your children by giving them "the talk" too young. Wait until they're good and ready. It may vary for each child, but usually a Mennonite is mature enough for this conversation sometime in their late 30s or early 40s. Approach them after the evening milking one day and say, "*Na*, Peter, I think it's time we had a little chat yet."

3. Use plenty of farm animal analogies. Remember, you've got to make the topic relatable. A tour through a nearby farrow-to-finish barn is a great idea. Not only will they learn about reproduction, but they'll also answer that age-old Mennonite question: "Mommy, where does farmer sausage come from?"

4. Defer to the wisdom of Elder Stoesz. Every Mennonite church has a lifelong bachelor who's a self-proclaimed expert on marriage, sex, and child-rearing. If you have any questions about sex, Elder Stoesz will quickly haul out his Bible concordance and find the answer. He's knowledgeable, eager, and easy to find as he's usually milling about the lobby after the service just waiting to tell some young people what to do. What a valuable resource!

5. Choose the right location. I know you're probably thinking that the tractor is the best place for every serious conversation, but not this one! When having a shocking and traumatic discussion like this you need to stay clear of heavy machinery. It's important to find a place that's private and safe. Find a time when the MCC store isn't very busy, then head to the changing rooms and get yourselves neighbouring stalls. Speak just barely loud enough for your child to hear you through the wall. It's almost like Catholic confession. Very discreet!

6. Use as many detailed personal examples as possible. No need to be shy. You can start by saying something like, "When your mother and I were first married, we didn't know what we were doing either, but we ..." and then fill in the details from there.

7. Calmly assure them that all their feelings are completely unnatural and need to be repressed. A young person may be confused about their changing bodies, so it's your job to pass on the Mennonite tradition of repression, bewilderment, and the feeling that everything about the human body is sinful. Have them repeat the Mennonite sex education mantra: "Don't look. Don't touch. It's all from the Devil."

Mennonite Writer Finally Sells Book to Non-Relative
CALGARY, AB

History was made last night after literary icon Margaret Banman-Lepp became the first Mennonite author ever to sell a book to a non-relative. The feat took place at the launch of her 23rd publication entitled *Of Solitude and Flax: Tales from the Banman-Lepp Archives*.

"I was sitting there signing copies for all the Banmans and Lepps who showed up, when out of the corner of my eye, what did I see? A mysterious woman I didn't recognize at all," said Banman-Lepp. "I nearly fell out of my chair. In more than 30 years of book signing, she was the first person I've ever had to ask for a name."

The mysterious non-related customer bought two copies, saying she was going to give one to a friend who, apparently, is also not related in any way to Banman-Lepp.

"I was in tears," said Banman-Lepp. "I've won awards, I've received great reviews, I've been on the front page of the *MB Herald* more times than I can count, but never did I imagine I'd make a sale to someone more distantly related than a great-aunt."

Of Solitude and Flax has reportedly sold more than 1,000 copies to Banmans and Lepps, plus the two copies purchased by that one woman outside the author's immediate family.

City to Replace Surveillance Cameras
with Mennonite Ladies
SASKATOON, SK

After a recent rash of petty theft, where locals saw cabbage rolls and fruit *vereniki* swiped from their window sills at an alarming rate, the Government of Saskatchewan has decided to hire Oma Ens, 83, of Saskatoon to head the new provincial Security and Crime Reduction program.

"Basically she'll just do what she already does," said Saskatchewan Premier Brad Wall. "Peer out her window, watch what's happening, and tell her friends at the quilting bee. Eventually it'll get around to us."

Beginning this Friday, Oma Ens will be observing everyone from the third-floor balcony of her Saskatoon retirement home, where she can get clear views of the entire province of Saskatchewan. Meanwhile, her friends Oma Nickel and Oma Berg will be working in shifts to monitor the lobby camera and taking notes on the folks coming in and out of the building.

"There will be no more *holubschi* thefts under my watch," said Oma Ens. "And while we're at it, did you see that Tina Epp? She was in Mr. Isaac's room all morning doing who knows what. She emerged in the early afternoon, only to stop by Mr. Loeppky's room for a quick game of crokinole. Then she spent the rest of the day playing Uno with the Doerksen sisters late into the night."

The new measure is estimated to save the province more than $5 billion in annual security costs, although those savings will be slightly dampened by the increased cost in knitting needles.

"It costs the province three knitting needles in exchange for every name they give us," said Wall. "These Mennonite *omas* drive a hard bargain, but it's still cheaper than hiring some dude to watch surveillance tape all day."

In addition to nabbing a few petty thieves, Oma Ens and her colleagues are apparently able to give a complete list of the comings and goings of every person in the province over the past two weeks, although the details get a little iffy every day at 6:00 p.m. when *Jeopardy!* is on.

Mennonites Rush to Get Their Cars Outside During Hailstorm

ST. CATHARINES, ON

Mennonites across the Niagara region were in a panic to get their cars out onto the streets last night after a record-setting hailstorm struck the peninsula.

"With golf-ball-sized hail like that, how else can I protect my investment but by making sure my '98 Caravan is out there to take the full brunt of the weather?" said Mr. Voth. "You don't get many opportunities like this!"

Voth received a notification on his smartphone from the Mennonite Weather Service, which alerts locals to inclement weather that might be economically advantageous.

"As soon as I got the message, I rushed to pull my minivan out of the garage," said Voth, who says he won't be happy unless he gets a full write-off and a gift card for Arby's. "Everyone in my neighbourhood was parking on the street too. I'm glad to see they're all as fiscally responsible as I am."

As an extra precaution, Voth stripped naked and ran out into the storm hoping maybe, just maybe, to be struck by lightning.

"If I survive," said Voth, modestly covering himself for *Daily Bonnet* reporters. "I might get a free week or two in the hospital. That'll really save on the grocery bill."

Voth is also hosting an upcoming church Bible study event where he plans to teach attendees how to get new shingles on your roof every month or so with nothing but a hockey stick and a little bit of gumption.

Mennonite Woman Consults *Fifty Shades of Grey* for Wardrobe Advice

HILLSBORO, KS

Local senior Helen Groening was shocked by the misleading content of the popular book *Fifty Shades of Grey*, which she purchased used at the local MCC store hoping for advice on how to update her wardrobe.

"Currently I've got 20 or 30 shades of grey in my closet," said Groening. "Some of the ladies in the care home have close to 40 but, *oba*, never in all my years have I heard of anyone with 50 shades of grey."

The sheer volume of grey shades was what initially drew Groening's attention to the book, but the intriguing story of forbidden romance kept her reading for a while.

"It wasn't quite what I was expecting," said Groening. "I mean, back on the farm we did use the belt if we needed to … but not like that."

Baffled by the book, Groening plans to track down its former owner, Melanie Dueck, who had scrawled her name in pen on the title page sometime before donating the book to the thrift store.

"Miss Dueck should be able to explain the book to me," said Groening. "I don't really understand it, but what I do know is that it has very little to do with maintaining a monochromatic wardrobe."

Meddachschlop After 60: 5 Tips for Mennonite Seniors

As we age, many things that we took for granted as young Mennonites start to become more difficult. Plowing is hard on the back. Hitting that high note during *Saengerfest* becomes a challenge. Interest in raw *foarmaworscht* begins to wane. However, some topics are more difficult to talk about than others. That is why *The Daily Bonnet* has consulted with industry experts to discuss the most taboo subject of them all: *meddachschlop* after 60.

Here are the top tips from our experts:

1. Make a plan for *meddachschlop*. Between visits with the grandkids and a round of golf at the Fly-In, finding time for *meddachschlop* can be difficult. It might even be that Sunday after church is not the best time for you. Perhaps a Wednesday afternoon right after *Family Feud* is more your speed.

2. Leave room to be spontaneous. While having a plan is important, it's also a good idea to be spontaneous with your *meddachschlop*. Maybe you just had a big dinner and need to lie down for a bit. Maybe the *frindschauft* finally left and you're in need of a good 15-minute *meddachschlop*. Let it happen! The dishes can wait!

3. Don't worry if things don't work out. Many older Mennonites suffer from *meddachschlop* anxiety and worry that they just don't have the energy that they used to. When it comes to *meddachschlop*, however, the less energy you have, the better. You're trying to get a good nap in after all, aren't you?

4. Try something new! It's never too late to try something new with your afternoon nap routine. Maybe Agnes can sleep on the left this time. Maybe you'll leave the lights on. Perhaps you'll crank up the *Back to the Bible* broadcast and see what that does. Don't be afraid to broaden your *meddachschlop* horizons.

5. Consider your health. Studies have shown that afternoon naps with your partner can do wonders. Couples who *meddachschlop* regularly live two to three years longer than those who don't. Stay young; have plenty of *meddachschlop*!

So, there you have it. Try these tips this afternoon and let us know how it turns out!

How the Gingerich Stole Christmas
By Dr. Stoltzfus

Every Menno down in Waterloo liked Christmas a lot,
Except for Mr. Gingerich who certainly DID NOT!
Gingerich hated Christmas! The whole Christmas season!
The gifts and the songs and that old Mrs. Friesen.
"Oh, why did we let a Russian Menno in here?"
Wondered sad Mr. Gingerich with a sigh and a sneer.
The Mennonites of Waterloo had wanted a change,
"But their food is so foreign and their accent is strange!"
The Friesens were permitted, if just for a test,
And Friesens, being Friesens, did what Friesens did best.
They baked and they boiled and they cooked up a feast
Of *schmaunt fat* and cracklings and lots of roast beast.
But old Mr. Gingerich could not stand to eat.
The sausage was too salty and the syrup was too sweet.
"Soon it will be Christmas and then what will that bring?
Nothing but presents and games and four-part singing!"
He went to the church and looked down from the top.
"They can do it in Winkler, but here it must stop!"
So he hatched up a scheme, while the rest were in song.
"I have an idea: let's say everything's wrong!"
He spoke to the elders who agreed with his plan.
"Joy can't be from God. It must be from man."
And so it came out, as if by royal decree:
"Christmas must end!" said the elders with glee.
"Laughing and playing and speaking out of place
Will get you a shunning and a pie in the face."
So the Mennos became sombre and the season got dark,
The lights were turned off and the whole town was stark.
There was no celebration of the saviour's birth,
No gifts and no gatherings and certainly no mirth.
Until little Cindy of Waterloo stood out from the crowd.

"I have something to say, if I may be allowed.
I think we've been fooled, we've followed their trick.
Why must Christmas be dreadful, and awful, and sick?"
Then wee little Cindy held out her wee little hand.
"Hello, Mr. Gingerich," she said as she helped him to stand.
Then she hauled out a hymnal and turned to a page.
At first he was furious and started to rage.
Cindy grabbed for his hand, his fingers like sticks,
And pointed to the words of Hymn 606.
With tears in his eyes, Gingerich started to glow,
"Praise God from whom all blessings flow."
"It's been years," he said, "since I've sung this song."
"It's been years," he repeated, "it should not have been so long."
"Bring on Christmas!" he said with a smile,
"Let's get out the Dutch Blitz and stay for a while!"
So the Mennos in Waterloo decided to play,
While Mr. Gingerich's heart grew three sizes that day.

Open Casting Call in Winkler for New *Planet of the Abes* Movie

WINKLER, MB

Abes across the Pembina Valley will be flocking to the freshly paved parking lot at the EMBCC church this weekend to try out for a part in the new *Planet of the Abes* movie.

"*Oba jo*! Finally a movie for me," said Abe Warkentin, who has just wrapped up a three-night performance as Captain von Trapp in the Winkler production of *The Sound of Music*. "Abe Harder doesn't stand a chance! And Abe Kehler better watch his back! I'm certain I'll get to play the lead Abe!"

The movie stars Charlton Heston Jr. as an astronaut who lands on a strange and mysterious planet where Abes have taken over. Thankfully for the protagonist, the Abes all speak fluent Low German.

"We scouted filming locations all over the world," said producer Franklin Schroeder, "but we found that Winkler gave us both a friendly tax structure and the nearly endless supply of Abes that our production required."

Hundreds of Winkler Abes, young and old, will be needed for the film, says Schroeder.

"Even if you're not fluent in Plautdietsch, we can use you as an extra," said Schroeder. "Let me put it plainly: if you're an Abe and don't have a criminal record, come on down and be in our movie!"

Schroeder was reluctant to reveal too many spoilers, but says the movie has a special twist ending where the astronauts find out they were in *jantsied* all along.

Grandma Rescued After Literally Knitting Herself Into a Corner

MORDEN, MB

Margaret Toews, 91, of Morden was rescued by emergency personnel this weekend after she inadvertently knitted herself into a corner that she could not escape.

"That's what I do all day," said Toews from her apartment at the Sprinkled Water Manor. "I *tjnette* scarves for the grandchildren. Toques. Mittens. *Wolljacke*. Well, I guess I got a little disoriented or something because I was feeling a little *hungrijch* and decided to microwave a bit of *borscht* with whipping cream thrown in once, but when I tried to get up out of my chair, I discovered that I was completely surrounded by knitting. I had tied myself into the corner yet."

Toews explained that she was trapped in her apartment for more than four hours before her friend Elma Engbrecht, 87, knocked on the door.

"*Mensch ekj saj*! I'm sure thankful we had that Scrabble date," said Toews. "Otherwise I might never have been discovered."

However, when Engbrecht attempted to extract Toews from the spiderweb of knitting, she soon found herself entangled as well.

"I don't know how it happened," said Engbrecht. "I tried to *schuppse* Margaret's arm out from under the yarn, but then I kept being jabbed by the needle and ... well, somehow we were both ravelled up in the mess."

The pair called for help and their cries were heard by lonely Mr. Thiessen, though as soon as the women discovered it was *Truärijch* Thiessen who wanted to help, they immediately said, "*Na*, we're just fine, Henry," and sent him away.

"Ever since his Susie passed away, he's been trying to get close to Margaret," explained Engbrecht. "A little too close, if you ask me."

By 4:30 p.m. the pair was notably absent at supper, and this is when they were discovered by Sprinkled Water staff, who immediately contacted the fire department.

"Mrs. Toews and Mrs. Engbrecht are resting and doing just fine," said Sprinkled Water spokesperson Jennifer Dueck, "though it's lucky for all of us that the Jaws of Life were available when we needed them."

Mennonite Man Confuses Genealogy Website for Dating App

NEW BOTHWELL, MB

Aghast at the prices of more famous ancestry websites, budding young cheesemaker Adam Goertzen decided to subscribe to Grandma's Window, a much more affordable website dedicated exclusively to Russian Mennonite genealogy. The problem was, however, that as soon as Adam subscribed, he quickly became more interested in discovering who was single than who his ancestors were.

"Oh, look, Ashley Goertzen is just a year younger than me and she lives over there in Blumenhoff. I'm definitely swiping right!" said Goertzen. "Oh, and check out Madison Goertzen's profile! Twenty-five years old, a Steinbach Bible College graduate, and set to inherit 500 acres' worth of gravel pits near Grunthal!"

Goertzen spent hours scouring the website and compiling a list of distant cousins he could date.

"I have more cousins than I even realized," said Goertzen, "and many of them are single!"

With the decline in family gatherings as of late, Goertzen claims the genealogy website is one of the few places left for a young man like himself to find a potential life partner.

"Sophie Goertzen (1993 – present) seems like a catch," said Goertzen. "Looks like she's a third cousin and even works at the Co-op!"

Goertzen says he wishes the website had pictures and biographical information, but that baptismal records are more than enough for him.

Top 10 Most Badass Russian Mennonite Surnames

If there's one thing Russian Mennonites—particularly MBs and GCs—have in common, it's the unrelenting pursuit of hipness. To make it a little easier on everyone, *The Daily Bonnet* has created this convenient list of common Russian Mennonite surnames ranked in order of their perceived coolness.

10. Reimer—This name is a little too common to be truly badass but derives some credibility from its association with southern Manitoba's first rapper, Corny Reimer, and his sidekick EMC Hammer. 55% badass.

9. Fehr—There's nothing Mennonites like more than fairness … unless you're a woman or young person. But anyway, Fehr is a pretty fair name. Not intimidating or worldly, but straightforward and to the point. 61% badass.

8. Loewen—At first glance, this common Russian Mennonite surname is not cool at all, but the fact that it means "lion" gives it some points. It also gets a few more points for being the name of a tasty Munich beer. 73% badass.

7. Berg—Berg means "mountain." Mennonites like mountains, which is why all your relatives left the Prairies to go live near them in beautiful Chilliwack or suburban Calgary. 74% badass.

6. Hamm—Mennonites are huge consumers of pork. It is by far our favourite source of protein, sodium, and fat. Being named after a Mennonite's favourite snack is pretty cool, I must say. 80% badass.

5. Voth—I have no clue what this name means, but it's short and rhymes with "goth" so that's pretty hip ... I think. 81% badass.

4. Harms—Mennonites have scattered all across the world to avoid being harmed. People with this surname are effortlessly cool. You don't mess with a Harms or you'll be harmed. 85% badass.

3. Wall—A wall is a powerful symbol, used by both Pink Floyd and Donald Trump. This gets points only for the Pink Floyd association. 86% badass.

2. Fast—Add any first name to this surname and it's instantly just a little bit cooler. It makes the bearer seem like they could be the lead singer of a punk rock band. 91% badass.

1. Funk—How a people that don't dance got a surname like this is beyond me. Well, it is what it is. In secret, all Mennonites like to funk it up with some Prince or Sly and the Family Stone tunes once in a while. James Brown was reportedly a big fan of this surname. 95% badass.

'Winkler Humility' March Offers Stark Contrast to 'Morden Pride'

WINKLER, MB

Days after Morden's first ever Pride march, a confused yet earnest Mennonite man from neighbouring Winkler decided to hold a march of his own.

"*Dietja*, those Mordeners are always so proud and smiling and having a great time!" exclaimed Winkler resident Mr. Jacob Klassen. "But what do they have to be proud of over there? A couple dinosaur bones and a Chicken Chef?"

Klassen believes this Morden Pride thing must have something do with having "fewer Mannanites out there yet."

"Mannanites are the humblest people in the whole world!" proclaimed Klassen. "So to prove our humility, I asked averyone to come on Monday afternoon for the first annual Vankla Humility march!"

The Winkler Humility march featured a couple dozen dour-looking Mennonites, mostly Klassen's *frindschauft*, all wearing black and walking down Mountain Avenue flagellating themselves.

"It's the biggest event of the summer!" said Klassen. "We marched from the MCC to the Co-ops and back."

The humblest person in attendance at the Humility march, Klassen's second cousin on the Kehler side, was the very proud winner of a round-trip week-long vacation to Morden.

6 Hospitalized After Jesus Takes the Wheel

Four Ebys and two Zehrs were rushed to the hospital in Kitchener this week after Mr. Noah Eby decided to relinquish his driving duties and let Jesus take over.

"I was heading up the 85 towards Elmira when I decided it was time to let Jesus take the wheel," explained Eby. "So I just put the cruise control on and scooched over to the passenger seat."

Having recently aligned the car's wheels, Eby says everything seemed to be going fine, until they had to make a sharp left turn on Listowel.

"The car jumped the curb, went straight on through the Esso lot, and slammed into the Zehrs," said Eby. "Luckily there were only minor injuries, but this whole thing has really shaken us up. We're all really starting to question the theological veracity of country music lyrics."

Eby has been charged with Driving Under the Influence of Carrie Underwood and, if convicted, could face up to three years in prison listening to that song nonstop. Thankfully for Eby, his pastor has been a real source of support in his time of need.

"I'm warning everyone against taking Carrie Underwood too literally," said Pastor Johan. "In terms of driving advice derived from Christian pop culture, it seems to me that 'God Is My Co-Pilot' is a much safer option."

Introducing the All-New Mennonite Enneagram!

According to the ancient and mystical Mennonite Ennea-gram written by Richard Reimer and Andreas Hiebert, there are nine distinct Mennonite personality types. Which one are you?

TYPE ONE: The Need to Make the Perfect Quilt—Ones tend to be very obsessive about all things quilting. They can be easily identified by the thimbles on their fingers and bits of loose thread on their blouses.

TYPE TWO: The Need to Be Kneaded—Everyone wants to feel kneaded. Twos usually end up on the receiving ends of many trips to the *trajchtmoaka*.

TYPE THREE: The Need to Succeed Your Father at the Church Pew Factory—Type Threes have a very strong desire to take over the family business and are willing to do anything, including but not limited to backstabbing Onkel Pieta, in order to achieve their goal of taking over the church pew factory.

TYPE FOUR: The Need to Be Spashal—Some Mennonites need to feel *seea* spashal all the time yet. They yust can't go a day once without doing someting a little spashal and nice for Elizabeth.

TYPE FIVE: The Need to Perceive What the Neighbours Are Doing—Type Fives are inquisitive folks who like to know what's happening, even if it means peering through the neighbour's basement window to see if the rumours are true about their forbidden pool table.

TYPE SIX: The Need for a Secure Place to Park Your Combine—It's not easy parking a combine. Even with the wide boulevards of Vankla, it can be trouble. Type Sixes will never give up a good tractor and/or combine parking spot once they've nabbed it.

TYPE SEVEN: The Need to Avoid Your Pain-in-the-Ass Cousin Johan—Type Sevens are particularly averse to the annoying habits of cousin Johan. If only he'd keep his rubber boots and dandelion wine to himself!

TYPE EIGHT: The Need to Be Against the Wind During Manure-Spreading Season—Some say that Eights have an oppositional disorder, but really they just want to be against the wind. The aromas of the farm provide them with soothing memories of their childhoods. Remarkably, they also don't mind being against the wind when Onkel Jakob walks by.

TYPE NINE: The Need to Avoid Clean-Up Duty After *Faspa*—Type Nines always scoot out of church early to avoid helping out with the clean-up. Type Nines are often pastors' sons.

'Free Dance Lessons' Creates Profound Existential Crisis in Mennonite Town

FERNHEIM COLONY, PARAGUAY

Residents of a small Mennonite community experienced deep existential angst on Wednesday when signs went up across town offering "Free Dance Lessons."

"As a Mennonite, I'm obligated to take anything that's free, but also as a Mennonite, I'm obligated not to move my body to the sound of any sort of music," said David Rempel, 25, of the Fernheim region, who just completed a Master's degree in philosophy at Asunción University and recently returned home to take a job cleaning the stalls at his father's dairy farm. "Alas, this is the lot that Mennonites have been handed."

The signs offering free dance lessons appeared all over town in the middle of the night, causing considerable consternation in the town's population the next morning.

"This is more or less what Nietzsche called *amor fati,* which is the resignation to love your condition and fate, whether good or bad," remarked Rempel, treating a nearby udder with teat dip, while his father, Klaus, spread the straw and nodded in agreement.

"Free dance lessons," continued David, scooting over to the next set of udders, "are exactly what 19th century Danish existentialist Søren Kierkegaard was talking about in *Fear and Trembling*! This dilemma reaches into the very core of our Mennonite existence and identity. Once I saw that sign, I finally understood what Kierkegaard meant by 'subjectivity as truth'!"

Klaus, having not a clue what the heck his son was blathering on about, just shrugged his shoulders and smiled, grateful to have some more help around the farm. Meanwhile, David kicked the manure off his boots, ran into the house, and came back with his weathered copy of Jean-Paul Sartre's philosophical tome *Being and Nothingness.*

"Sartre talks about this too!" David said with great enthusiasm to his baffled father. "When a Mennonite is offered free dance lessons, he is forced to act in what Sartre calls 'bad faith,' a concept similar to self-deception, whereby people conform to social pressures rather than their authentic self!"

Having milked all the cows, and now filled with a new sense of angst that he will likely never fully comprehend, Klaus nodded his head and said, "*Na jo dan,*" and proceeded to start the tractor.

Mennonite Grandmas Frantically Fill Paper Bags with Peanuts

NORTH KILDONAN, MB

With just a few days left before the annual MB Church Christmas pageant, grandmothers throughout southern Manitoba have been working in shifts to fill thousands of paper bags with peanuts. The paper bags, also known as *tüte*, are a Mennonite holiday tradition and are usually filled to the brim with unsalted peanuts, one withered Mandarin orange, and a package of Juicy Fruit gum.

"It's hard to keep up with the demand. We've even had to add an evening shift," said *tüte* factory manager Mrs. Evelyn Martens. "But we've got to have these paper bags filled and ready to be consumed before opening night of the MB Church musical production of *Willy Warkentin and the Cottage Cheese Factory.*"

Martens says it's hard to find good help these days and complains that some of the grandmas have been slacking off, telling jokes, or singing German hymns while they work.

"We don't have time for that '*Stille Nacht, heilige Nacht*' nonsense. We have paper bags to fill," said a visibly stressed Martens. "The children are going to come barging in right after the concert expecting a *tüt* with their name on it, and we can't disappoint them."

All the MB children have been instructed by their parents to act really excited about the paper bags, even though they're mostly looking forward to getting home and opening that package under the tree that looks just the right size to fit a PlayStation.

7 Signs a Mennonite Man Is Just Not That Into You

If you're interested in hooking up with a man who catches chickens for a living, you've come to the right place. However, in the competitive dating scene of 21st century Rosengart or Gnadenfeld, it's increasingly important to be able to pick up on any subtle hints that Abe or Corny is just not that into you. The next time you're out clubbing in *jantsied* and you see these signs, you'll know not to waste your time. (You're probably too good for him anyway.)

1. He buys you flowers ... from the MCC. This is a classic Mennonite-man tactic. All the wilted funeral flowers that don't get buried along with the deceased get sent to the thrift store where they're purchased by Mennonite men on first dates. They may smell nice, but they're a sure-fire sign your relationship is dead in the water.

2. He makes only half-hearted attempts at cleaning his rubber boots. Any self-respecting Mennonite man will clean up a little bit when he wants to impress a date. He'll usually put on a pair of socks with sandals. That being said, rubber boots are acceptable dating attire, just so long as there isn't too much pig shit on them—if the layer of manure exceeds a quarter-inch thick, you know you're in trouble.

3. He says "*na jo dan*" the moment you approach him. Of all the Plautdietsch phrases, this is the worst. Literally, it means "well yes then," but in reality it's only used when Mennonites want to get rid of other Mennonites, such as when Taunte Lina and Onkel Jake overstay their welcome. This phrase is certain death to any potential dating relationship.

4. He brings his sister Nettie along. Nettie's a likeable woman, of course. I mean, who doesn't like Nettie? We all like Nettie … but not on a date. Even though she's your cousin, you shouldn't let him bring her along. It means he doesn't want to be alone with you for fear you'll put your hand on his knee.

5. He keeps glancing across the room at Elder Penner's daughter. If his eyes continue wandering over to the young woman with the *düak* over in the corner, you know he's not the one for you. Don't even try to win him over. Unless you happen to have a killer collection of flower dresses and brown nylons, you don't stand a chance.

6. He approaches you at the bar and orders a round of tap water. Not only is he too cheap to buy you a shot of yerba mate, but he also wants to keep you as sober-minded as possible so that you don't get any ideas of slipping your hand beneath his suspenders and … well, you know where things go from there.

7. He says he's been given the "gift of celibacy." In theory, this gift is possible to have: think of monks and missionaries. However, it's also a convenient way for a Mennonite man to pretend to be spiritually pure when all he really wants is to get with Nita Sawatzky instead of you.

Schekjbenjel Retires After 40 Years of Service
REINFELD, MB

Celebrated across the province for his impeccable *schek-jbenjel*ing, Klaas B. Kehler of Reinfeld is set to retire later this month after a four-decade-long career. Kehler was renowned for his ability to go back to the truck and get the nail gun, and also to hold the ladder while Helmut Guenther goes up on the roof.

"It's been a good long run," said Kehler. "I've gone and gotten stuff for more competent workers for decades, and now it'll be nice to take a break for once."

During his career, Kehler worked for Guenther Construction, Herman's Electrical, and briefly in the 1980s at an auto mechanic shop in Plum Coulee where he held and got stuff for Abram Peters.

"He was an excellent getter of stuff," explained Peters. "He didn't work for me for very long before he moved up in the world as *schekjbenjel* for a local construction crew. I mean, I don't blame him. Given the chance, I'd fetch a Robertson screwdriver from the red toolbox for Helmut Guenther anytime."

Kehler intends to spend most of his time with his grandchildren now that he's retired.

"I plan to go around and ask them whether they're 'working hard or hardly working,'" said Kehler with a chuckle. "Then I'll send them to the truck for the wood stretcher."

Mennonite Woman Sets Personal Best
by Deadlifting 50 Mason Jars
TORONTO, ON

Angela Funk, 31, of Toronto set a new personal record at the gym this week by deadlifting 50 mason jars filled with Oma Funk's extra-thick strawberry jam.

"I've been killing it lately," said Funk, wiping down the bench. "In just six months I've nearly doubled my mason jar lifting capacity."

Funk is proud of her accomplishment but says she's not quite sure how to program mason jars into her Fitbit.

"Plus, I mean, these jars are filled with some pretty dense jam. It's not like it was chicken stock or something," explained Funk. "Now that I've reached my deadlift goal, I'm going to work on opening the jars, but I'm not sure I'm quite ready for that yet."

Funk says her new goal is to open one of Oma's mason jars without running water over it or tapping it with a spoon, but worries if she spends too much time perfecting her opening technique, she'll lose all the gains she made on the mason jar deadlift.

Mennonite Dog Breeder Creates New Breed, the 'Low-German Shepherd'

WINKLER, MB

Expert dog breeder Mr. Peter Fehr of Winkler has worked for more than three decades to create a new breed: the Low-German Shepherd. Thanks to a lot of blood, sweat, and tears, as well as the prayers of the entire Fehr clan, his hard work has finally paid off.

"I tried feeding his mother *roll kuchen* and *plautz*, but it didn't have the results I was axpacting," said Fehr. "I found out the hard way dat the only ting what works is to take the mother to evening service for a year or so. Dan the puppies come out just right!"

The new puppies, who bark in fluent Plautdietsch, are the first of their kind, but Fehr promises they will not be the last.

"*Jauma lied*! There are peoples in Vankla who want a good Low-German Shepherd yet," said Fehr. "I can't keep up with the demand."

Instead of responding to usual commands like "stay," "sit," and "roll over," the Low-German Shepherd will only obey orders such as "*bliewe*," "*sette*," and "*waut de schissjat!*"

"My little *hunt* Pieta is very spashal to me," said Fehr. "Nowadays Mr. Friesen and Corner Kornelsen and even the Petkau sisters have been coming to me and wanting to breed *met* Pieta, but I just say no. Pieta the Low-German Shepherd is not just breeding with anyone who shows a little interest yet!"

All the regular High-German Shepherds were very sad to hear the news and held a meeting in the Lutheran church to decide what to do.

"That Plautdietsch dog is putting us regular German

Shepherds out of work," said Heinz, a well-loved puppy in the area. "I think it's time we move to the city!"

Things have gotten so contentious in the local dog community that area Rottweilers and Dachshunds have petitioned the Winkler mayor to ban all attempts at breeding any more Low-German canines.

Porch Swing Launches Mennonite Grandma Into Neighbour's Yard
HEPBURN, SK

Mrs. Kathy Giesbrecht, 81, was rushed to the Hepburn Hospital for Farming and Sausage-Related Injuries last night after she was sent flying into the Goossen's yard during an overly vigorous session on the manor porch swing.

"I pushed my legs back and forth like they taught us during the porch-swing lessons I signed up for when I moved into this place," said Mrs. Giesbrecht. "As a Mennonite, I always give it my all. I guess, in this case, my all was a little too much."

Neighbour Mr. Goossen was tending to his BBQ when he saw Mrs. Giesbrecht soaring through the air above him.

"There I was, cooking up some wieners, and I looked up and what did I see? Mrs. Giesbrecht hurling toward my garden shed," explained Mr. Goossen. "She made a pretty spectacular landing, and once she brushed herself off, I invited her to stay for a hot dog or two."

Despite the cordial invitation, Mrs. Giesbrecht was in no condition to stay for Mr. Goossen's undercooked wieners.

"I've got a few broken bones and a couple bruises," said Mrs. Giesbrecht. "I'm just glad I landed in the rhubarb patch or I really might have been in rough shape."

Mrs. Giesbrecht says she most definitely will not be telling her grandchildren about the incident, lest they get any ideas.

Mennonites Excited for Latest Instalment in the 'Harder Boys' Series

BLUE CREEK COLONY, BELIZE

Mennonites are lining up outside bookstores throughout Belize in anticipation of the new Harder Boys adventure, *The Secret of Mrs. Schellenberg's Pantry*. The books, now numbering several hundred, feature wholesome brothers Johnny and Abram Harder who solve mysteries in the various Mennonite colonies of Central America.

"*Oba jo*, those Harder Boys get into quite the situations yet," said series author Franklin W. Doerksen. "We've got *The Secret of Mrs. Loewen's Düak*, *The Secret of the Plett Barn*, *The Secret of Mr. Reimer's Suspenders,* and *The Secret of the Missing Hymnals.*"

In each book, the Harder Boys, who reside in one of the nation's more conservative colonies, manage to solve mysteries without the use of any modern technology whatsoever.

"You'd be amazed what you can do with a good horse, a sharpened pencil, and a little bit of corn syrup," said Doerksen. "The Harder Boys are truly an inspirational pair!"

Doerksen claims that even after writing more than two hundred novels, he never has any trouble coming up with new ideas for Harder Boys books.

"In the latest adventure, Johnny hears strange sounds coming from the old Schellenberg place and goes to investigate," explained Doerksen. "He's quite distraught and recruits Abram to help him solve the mystery. Eventually they discover a half-butchered chicken, two catechism books, and an eerily warm butter churn. It doesn't take the Harder boys long to figure out that something is amiss."

The publisher, based in Blue Creek Colony, is also considering a series about a crime-solving Mennonite girl in a flower dress named Nancy Dueck.

Man With Obscure Mennonite Surname Feeling Totally Left Out

SWIFT CURRENT, SK

Local man Kenneth Mierau is sick and tired of all the attention given to "mainstream" Mennos like the Reimers and Penners and is demanding that the Mieraus be given their space on the pages of *The Daily Bonnet.*

"I can shout a good '*Donna!*' or '*Dietschlaunt!*' as well as any Friesen or Dueck," said Mierau. "It's time those *Daily Bonnet*ers realize that there's a lot more to Russian Mennonites than what you find on the street signs of Steinbach, Manitoba!"

Mierau claims that the average Plett or Thiessen doesn't even realize he's a Mennonite until he starts speaking Plautdietsch.

"My grandmother's *vereniki* are every bit as good as anything that Mrs. Kehler can come up with!" said Mierau. "It's time us Mieraus get what's coming to us!"

Mierau has started a committee for the recognition of uncommon Mennonite surnames. It already has over 100 members from the Kasdorf, Kampen, Pries, Adrian, and Olfert families.

"Obscure Mennonites of the world, unite!" yelled Mierau to a crowd that had gathered in the local MB church basement.

Mierau says he had to pay $200 to rent the basement for his meeting, since no one believed that anyone with a surname like his could actually be a church member.

Grandpa Wiebe Kjnipses 12 Twenties in a Row
WINKLER, MB

More than 1,000 Wiebes and other talented *kjnips*ers gathered in Winkler last night for the 50th annual Wiebestock Music and *Kjnips*ing Arts Festival, but it was Grandpa Cornelius B. Wiebe, 83, who left the lasting impression after *kjnips*ing a record 12 twenties in a row. At the rate of a toonie per *kjnipse*, he earned himself quite the pile of cash.

"It was twenty after twenty. I was on fire," said Wiebe. "I just kept on *kjnips*ing and *kjnips*ing until they all were *kjnips*ed right into that hole yet."

After a regular *kjnipsbrat* match against the uncles, Grandpa Wiebe got all the Wiebe men (and Wiebe boys too) to empty their wallets onto the table. The one who *kjnips*ed the most twenties, he explained, would get to keep the money.

"I knew they didn't stand a chance," said Wiebe. "That young Colin over there? His *kjnips*ing technique is all wrong. It was no wonder he only *kjnips*ed three twenties in 10 tries. That's some pretty pathetic *kjnips*ing if you ask me."

Wiebe has been honing the art of *kjnips*ing ever since he was in primary school.

"When I was just a wee *kjnips*er, I *kjnips*ed my way into Grace Epp's heart," said Wiebe, "and we've been *kjnips*ing together ever since."

Wiebe promises to tithe 10 percent of his *kjnipsbrat* earnings and then treat Grace to a nice dinner at Ralph's.

Friesen Siblings Gather for 20-Year Home School Reunion
ALTONA, MB

It was a splendid occasion in Altona this past week as the Friesen siblings gathered at Mom and Dad's bungalow to celebrate their 20-year home school reunion.

"We're the graduating class of 1997," said Dave, who works at the local feed mill. "It's so great to reunite with the other students at 632 6th Avenue NE School."

Dave, along with his brothers Dan and Tim and sisters Anne and Sarah, all managed to finish school at more or less the same time back in 1997 and, although they all still live in Altona and see each other every other day, got emotional when reunited and began reminiscing about their home school grad.

"Dave was the valedictorian," said Sarah, who runs a local flower shop, "but I think he mostly got voted in because he threatened to rough up Tim and Anne if they didn't vote in his favour."

Back in 1997, Sarah was voted the homecoming queen, an honour that made her sister Anne furious with jealousy.

"I can't help it, but I've just been more popular than Anne ever since my sophomore year in home school," said Sarah. "Quite frankly, I'm surprised she showed up to the reunion."

All five students at 632 6th Avenue NE School graduated with honours, much to the excitement of Mrs. Friesen, their Biology, English, Plautdietsch, Phys Ed., Math, and History teacher, and Mr. Friesen, the overly strict, no-nonsense principal, both of whom were present for the reunion. Mr. and Mrs. Friesen retired from teaching the very next year.

Mennonite Author Writes Autobiography, Calls It a 'Novel'

HOCHFELD, MB

Legendary Mennonite author Jakob Dyck has made a career out of writing thinly veiled autobiographies and his latest novel, *Ice Cream Pails Full of Pain*, is no exception.

"They say you should write about what you know," said Dyck. "Well, I know the old tale of Mr. Reimer and the mysterious coins left behind on the restaurant table, or the tale of the indecisive Plett couple who spent all afternoon arguing about whether to go to Winkler or Morden Chicken Chef. The novel practically writes itself."

Dyck's reputation for "writing about what he knows" has caused considerable anxiety for residents in his hometown of Hochfeld.

"People get nervous around me. They're always wondering if something they do or say might appear in one of my novels," said Dyck. "Well, they have good reason to feel this way. Where do you think I get all my ideas?"

Dyck's most famous literary creation is a wise-cracking Mennonite boy named Johan Dueck, who lives in the small farming town of Neuenburg where he milks cows and pines after Maria Petkau. Dyck admits there are some parallels to his own life.

"What can I say? I led a pretty exciting life as a young lad. Might as well write about it," said Dyck. "Plus, I come from the long-standing Mennonite literary tradition of writing about your relatives and pretending it's fiction. It's a well-known fact that every single Mennonite novel ever written is just a memoir with changed names."

Dyck will be signing copies of *Ice Cream Pails Full of Pain* and a brand-new book of sonnets called *Longing for Faspa and Other Poems* this Sunday afternoon at the Hochfeld Manor.

How to Tell if a Mennonite Is Flirting With You

When it comes to romance, Mennonites are tough nuts to crack, or should I say, tough *zoats* to *knack*. So how do you know if you're being flirted with? It's not so easy, but when it comes to Menno-dating, there are a few obvious tells that will give it away. Here they are!

1. She lets you beat her in a game of horseshoes. Let's face it, Mennonite women are pros when it comes to tossing used horseshoes at metal rods. So if she mysteriously misses that ringer in the last round of play, you know she did it because she's got the hots for you.

2. He begs you to come with him on the manure spreader. Think about it. Manure spreading is normally a solo endeavour, so if he suggests a ride-along, you know he wants to be more than just *frindschauft*.

3. She lets you see her ankles. Sometimes you might find yourself alone with a Mennonite woman behind the barn and things get a little frisky. If she lifts the hem of her dress up just enough to show off the gorgeous brown nylons on her ankles, you know she's the one for you.

4. She sits right next to you on your truck's bench seat. As a good Mennonite, you're likely driving a beat-up truck with a long bench seat in the front. If she comes up with some excuse to snuggle next to you, rather than perch next to the passenger window, you know there's love in the air.

5. His hand lingers on yours during a game of Dutch Blitz. Mennonites don't patronize movie theatres, so we never experience the classic moment where two lovers' hands meet in a buttery bag of popcorn. Instead, your hands may touch during a vigorous round of Dutch Blitz. If he allows his hand to linger on yours for more than the usual split second, you'll know that he's a keeper.

6. He adamantly denies that you're cousins. Even though your names are both in the *Reimer Book*, he might say it really doesn't count, or that you're only distantly related, or that "everyone is related if you go back far enough." Why say these things unless he is interested in pursuing a relationship with you?

Mannanite Man Can't Hear His Own Acksant
OSTERWICK, MB

Area man Peter Berg still insists after all these years that he doesn't have a Plautdietsch accent at all.

"At's all deeze *Enjelsch* who have da acksant yat," he said in perfectly fluent Low German. "I don't know vat dey're *jeräd*ing about vonce."

Berg is under the impression that averyone talks like him yet, and those who don't are the ones with the acksant.

"I talk da *Enjelsch* and I talk da Plautdietsch," explained Berg. "Yust becuz you're fram Vanapag doesn't mean you talk da *Enjelsch* corrackt yat."

Berg expressed frustration about a recent trip to Walmart in the big city where store employees couldn't understand what he was saying.

"I axed where da traktas are vonce," said Berg, "and da womens dare yust talled me 'it doesn't give such at Valmarts.' *Oba*, I was *truärijch* about dat."

Berg says from now on he plans to shop in Schteinback where nobody has an acksant and averyone talks yust like him yet.

Mennonite Teen Accused of Showing Too Much Ankle on Snapchat
LEAMINGTON, ON

Local Mennonite teen Kaitlyn Janzen, 18, will appear before the church deacon board on Tuesday evening after the youth group glow-bowling event to defend her "highly immodest" post on social media over the weekend.

"I was just showing off my new Doc Martens to my friends. I didn't think anything of it," said Janzen, who had just purchased the boots on a recent shopping trip to the city. "I tried to show as little ankle as possible, like the Bible commands, but I guess there was a bit of sock showing."

According to Janzen, she inadvertently sent a shot of her footwear to the ever-pious pastor's daughter Rachel Schmidt who immediately passed the image on to her elderly father.

"We just don't think young women should be going around exposing their ankles like this," said 73-year-old Rev. Schmidt. "We may have to ask her to apologize in front of the congregation. Oh, and this Doctor Martens fellow will have to account for his actions too!"

Janzen has been arraigned on charges of Being a Young Woman in a Mennonite Town and will be asked to refrain from posting images of her ankles, at least until next year when she goes to college at Conrad Grebel where ankles are, apparently, all the rage these days.

A Mennonite Guide to Card Games— Ranked in Order of Sinfulness

In an effort to add some clarity to a topic that has baffled Mennonites for centuries, *The Daily Bonnet* has devised a handy ranking system for the relative evilness of particular card games. In ascending order, the evilest card games are:

10. Rook—The great thing about Rook cards is that you're not using real playing cards which, apparently, are really, really bad. Instead of suits, you have colours, and that makes a world of a difference. Plus, you're playing in teams. Mennonites like teams. Rating: 0% sinful.

9. Dutch Blitz—Not sinful at all, unless someone breaks a finger and you don't apologize right away. Rating: 0% sinful but has potential to be somewhat sinful.

8. Uno—Also not sinful at all, but we much prefer if you refer to the game by its Plautdietsch name, *Een*. Rating: 0% sinful if played in Low German.

7. Big Boss, Little Boss—Also known by a variety of more colourful names, this game is sinful if you're using real playing cards. Please try to play this with Rook cards instead. Also, before commencing the game, please remind players that, as Mennonites, we do not believe in any kind of hierarchy. Consider playing Go Fish instead (or, perhaps, go actual fishing). Rating: 40% sinful.

6. Solitaire—Using playing cards is bad. However, at least with solitaire you're playing alone and are not being a stumbling block for anyone else struggling with card-playing. Rating: 50% sinful.

5. 52-Card Pickup—This is not so much a game as it is a trick you play on people. We like that there's no actual card-playing involved, and we like that a lot of time is spent literally picking cards off the floor, but given that the entire premise of the game is based on a lie, we cannot endorse it. Rating: 52% sinful.

4. Three-card Monte—This is a street scam designed to dupe tourists in European cities into giving up their money. As Mennonites, we've had more than enough trouble in Europe. Avoid this game. Rating: 70% sinful.

3. Poker—This game is often played by men with their buddies on a Saturday night and sometimes involves alcohol consumption. This is not the sort of fellowship we want to encourage, even if the buy-in is just $20. Rating: 81% sinful.

2. Blackjack—Not only does Blackjack use playing cards, but it also involves gambling and often takes place in a casino. Plus, the number 21 gives me the creeps. Rating: 100% sinful (unless you donate all your winnings to the church).

1. Strip Poker—Unless you're playing the Mennonite version, which involves adding layers of clothing, this game has everything wrong with it: playing cards, alcohol consumption, gambling, and cavorting with the opposite sex. Avoid at all costs. Rating: 100% sinful.

Local Chiropractor Specializes in Treating Mennonite Rubbernecking Injuries

CHORTITZ, MB

A southern Manitoba chiropractor has decided to focus his talents on addressing neck injuries caused by prolonged gawking and staring, which, he says, is a common affliction in Mennonite communities everywhere.

"Prolonged periods of rubbernecking can put a real strain on your cervical vertebrae," said chiropractor Isaac Letkeman. "I recommend that patients take a break from rubbernecking every 15 minutes or so. Get up, stare at someone else for a while, then go back to ogling those strange-looking Englishers from the city."

Letkeman says some of his patients come to see him after spending an entire weekend sitting in lawn chairs on the front lawn with a bag of *zoat*, staring and commenting on the occupants of each car as they pass by.

"I have no idea why they don't sit in their backyards where it's not so distracting, but I guess they just like to people-watch," said Letkeman. "It's nice that they're curious, but I wish they'd think about what this excessive rubbernecking is doing to their spinal alignment ..."

Letkemen's Rubbernecking Emporium is open six days a week, and does allow walk-ins, but he recommends that ailing Mennonites make an appointment so that they're not tempted to sit in the waiting room and stare at the other patients.

Mrs. Henry L. Funk Celebrates 50 Years of Using Her Husband's Name

KRONSGARTEN, MB

Local woman Mrs. Henry L. Funk, 71, is celebrating 50 years of never once using her own first name. Funk follows the Mennonite tradition of signing all her letters, postcards, and even legal documents by simply affixing the word "Mrs." in front of her husband's name.

"It all started when we were married at the Kronsgarten EMB back in 1966," said Mrs. Henry L. Funk. "Even though my Henry passed away years ago, I still find comfort in using his name, though the truth is I couldn't remember my first name even if I tried."

After a half century as Mrs. Henry L. Funk, Mrs. Henry L. Funk says she'd be happy to find some documentation from her early years.

"I'm pretty sure my maiden name was Loeppky," said Mrs. Henry L. Funk, "because all my spinster sisters are Loeppkys. But as for my first name, I have no clue. Was it Ruth? Betsy? Helen? Who remembers such things?"

Life as Henry L. Funk has not always been easy for Mrs. Henry L. Funk, but she says that over the years she's grown accustomed to all of her late husband's interests and hobbies.

"You should see the muskrat I trapped last winter," said Mrs. Henry L. Funk. "I may have no idea what my name is or what my own interests used to be, but I sure do know how to tan a hide and play a *brommtopp* ... just like Mr. Henry L. Funk."

Students Petition CMU for 'Hipster Discount'
WINNIPEG, MB

A group of freshmen students at Canadian Mennonite University in Winnipeg are petitioning the institution for a discount on their tuition fees because they claim they are something called "hipsters."

"Children of alumni, missionary kids, child prodigies—they all get discounts at places like this. It's time that young people with perfectly groomed beards and unnecessarily oversized glasses get a piece of the discount pie," said spokes-hipster Emily Björk-Friesen. "I think CMU benefits tremendously from having us in the student body and hipping up the place a bit."

After having long ago surpassed Steinbach Bible College and Providence University College in total hipster population, CMU is hoping to have even more Arcade Fire enthusiasts in their student body than the University of Winnipeg by the end of the term.

"In order to achieve our goal of having the most St. Vincent and Iron & Wine listeners in the province, we've got to let hipsters in at a discounted rate," said Björk-Friesen, a first-year Peace and Conflict Transformation Studies major. "If we can each get a free Joy Division T-shirt and a pour-over coffeemaker on the first day of classes, that would also be much appreciated."

It is not known whether CMU will take the request seriously, or risk losing their entire student body to the Creative Communications program at Red River College.

Mennonite Man Works His Usual 18 Hours on Labour Day
ABBOTSFORD, BC

Labour Day is just like any other day for local butcher Ike Siemens of the Abbotsford area, who spent a full 18 hours making farmer sausage like he always does.

"I don't take a day off unless it's the Lord's Day yet," explained Siemens, "and even then, sometimes I work if the ox has fallen into the well, so to speak."

Siemens is following the ancient Mennonite tradition of working such long hours that you have no time for sin, and says the temptations don't stop on holidays so neither should his sausage stuffing.

"When you've got a nice natural casing in your hand, you're not thinking about the sinful things of the world," said Siemens, tying the ends of a long roll of *foarmaworscht*. "I don't know what it is, but sausage just has this way of keeping my mind on higher things."

While Siemens is at work most of the day, he does stop by at home for a late lunch each afternoon, during which his wife and children sit in complete silence as the patriarch wolfs down a hearty bowl of *botta supp*. Siemens says he's unfamiliar with this thing called "Labour Day" and that it sounds kind of fishy to him.

"Never heard of that," he said. "It must be one of those sakular holidays the government creates to keep us Mennonites from working hard."

When asked whether he perhaps might be a workaholic, Siemens shrugged his shoulders and replied, "Ach, I've never even touched the stuff."

Mennonite Parents Use Low-German Code Language During Holiday Season
RIVERTON, MB

The Koops of Riverton have been speaking nonstop Plautdietsch this December in order to keep young Abigail and Mason from finding out what they're getting for Christmas.

"It's great, we can *jeräd* all day about Mason's new *flitzepee* or Abigail's new *poontje* and the kids will never find out," said Heather Koop, 31. "*Oba*, they'll be surprised on Christmas Day yet!"

The Koops have also been using Plautdietsch to discuss other touchy subjects, such as Grandpa's open-heart surgery and Mr. Loewen's affair with Mrs. Froese.

"I'm sure glad we never forced the kids to learn Low German," said Koop, turning down the volume on her Boney M. Christmas album, "or else I don't know how on earth the adults would be able to chat about Sally Poetker's unplanned pregnancy or Helmut Penner's drinking problem."

Unbeknownst to their parents, however, Abigail and Mason have been covertly taking Plautdietsch lessons from an older cousin who is offering lessons for the price of a single plastic bag of fresh cheese curds.

"We've been listening through the register for the past six weeks," said Abigail. "I know all about Mr. Unger's gambling problem and the Dueck's upcoming divorce. Learning Plautdietsch has been a real eye-opener."

Abigail and Mason also say they intend to act really surprised on Christmas morning, even though they've known about the pony and bicycle for months.

Dishes Are Miraculously Washed as Mennonite Man Naps on Sunday Afternoon
INMAN, KS

After devouring a delicious meal of *schintjefleesch* and fried potatoes, local man Norm Penner, 47, decided to unbutton his pants, kick up his feet, and lie down on the living room sofa.

"Sunday is a day of rest," said Penner. "I wouldn't want to have to put my eternal salvation at risk by picking up a dish rag."

Penner has made a habit of sitting on his ass and not helping out ever since he was a little boy. It's a proud Mennonite tradition he plans to pass on to his sons.

"I'm not sure how it happens, but somehow the table is cleared and the dishes are clean," said Penner. "It's amazing. The table is all messy, I go lie down for a nice *meddachschlop*, and when I wake up, the dining room is spotless. It's a miracle!"

The Miracle of the Washed Dishes is being attributed to the pious and devout faith of our Mennonite men.

"The only explanation I have for this miracle is that God must be blessing us men for our righteousness," said Penner. "I don't want to brag or anything, but I am a pretty darn righteous fellow."

The holy faith of Mennonite men has also been claimed as the cause behind the miraculous Taking Out of the Garbage, Lowering of the Toilet Seat, and Midnight Roll in the Hay.

Mennonite Man Insists on Wearing Suspenders to Nude Beach

PATRICIA BEACH, MB

Sun lovers at a Lake Winnipeg clothing-optional beach were a little shocked this weekend to see that Delbert Krahn from the West Reserve was unwilling to remove his suspenders before taking to the waters.

"I don't never take these things off, not even to shower," said Krahn, thumbs tucked behind his suspenders. "My only problem is what do I clip them to?"

Krahn searched for some time to find an appropriate appendage to which he could clip his suspenders, but after trying out all the options, he eventually gave up.

"In the end, I had to employ a bit of duct tape, but I think it worked out pretty swell," said Krahn. "My only worry is just what kind of a tan line I'm going to be left with."

Krahn says he wasn't sure if there were any other Mennonites at the beach, though he did notice a few flower dresses sitting in a pile under a picnic table.

"I'm hoping Liza Martens shows up," he remarked. "She just loves me in these suspenders."

Friesen Woman to Become Froese
ROSETOWN, MB

The Froeses and Friesens of Rosetown are pleased to announce the engagement of Alex Froese, 25, to Samantha Friesen, 23. The proposal took place as soon as the snow fell this winter and the happy couple is planning a June wedding at which time Friesen will officially become Froese.

"I'm really excited," said Friesen, showing off her half carat diamond ring. "Usually I'm a Friesen in June, but this year I'll be completely Froese."

The Froese-Friesen wedding is set to take place on the Froese farm, which will be crawling with both Froeses and Friesens from out of town.

"I wasn't sure if Samantha's fiancé was one of those 'frays' or 'froze' Froeses," said the elder Mrs. Friesen. "I'm glad to hear he pronounces it correctly."

Despite the June wedding date, Friesens and Froeses in attendance are strongly encouraged to bring along a warm sweater, just in case.

"Bring a scarf too while you're at it," said Friesen. "It can get kind of chilly at night. I know how sensitive Friesens and Froeses can be and certainly don't want any Froeses to freeze."

'Twas the Night Before Mennonite Christmas

'Twas the night before Mennonite Christmas, when all
    through the house,
Not a Penner was stirring, not even Onkel Klaus;
The *tüte* were all eaten, the halva was all gone,
I was lying next to Martha wearing my favourite long johns;

The *tjinja* were nestled all snug in one bed,
While visions of *plümemoos* danced in their heads;
And Martha in her *düak*, and me filled with hope,
Of a quick Christmas snuggle on this long winter's *schlop*,

When out on the yard there arose such a melee,
That I sprang from the bed; "*Waut es met die!*"
To the Loewen window I flew at a furious pace,
With Martha at my side wearing nothing but lace.

The moon lit up the scene as I opened the curtain,
Who might it be? I sure was not certain,
When what to my Mennonite eyes did appear,
But eight tiny church elders dressed in winter gear,

And a little old man, standing square in our lawn,
This man, I assumed, must be Pastor Krahn.
In English he yelled and in Dietsch just the same,
He whistled, and shouted, and called them by name:

"Now, REIMER! now, KLASSEN! now, THIESSEN and EPP!
On, BROESKY! on, BERGEN! on, MARTENS and LEPP!
To the top of the roof! and in through the door!
If we have to, we'll drill a hole in the floor!"

They peered in our windows, self-righteous and loud;
They were looking for presents that were not allowed.
"What's this I see? A TV set?
A radio, a pool table, an Elvis cassette?"

They took all the things that they thought were wrong,
They took them while smiling and singing a song:
"Throw it in here! That goes in my sack!"
"An electric guitar? You aren't getting this back!"

Pastor Krahn seemed quite pleased and scratched at his belly,
That shook like a salad made of whipped cream and jelly.
They were about to escape with our toys and our rings;
They had all our names, they had all our things;

Then Martha approached, and started to sing,
"Silent Night, Holy Night"; her voice fit for a king.
She sang all three verses and another in German,
The elders uneasy; she sure had them squirmin'.

A crowd soon had gathered and joined her in song,
"We won't let them tell us what's right and what's wrong."
We sang and we prayed and we grabbed back our toys
That we wrapped up again for our girls and our boys.

The elders stood 'round and admitted defeat,
"Let's sing that again; the melody's sweet."
Pastor Krahn was now standing all on his own,
"Well, I suppose a pool table is okay in the home."

He sprang to his sleigh with his elders in tow,
"Mrs. Penner's in charge now; as for us, we must go."
And I heard him exclaim, as he drove out of sight—
"HAPPY CHRISTMAS TO ALL, AND TO ALL A
     GOOD-NIGHT!"

BROODASCHAUFT

(A CHURCH MEETING)

Mennonite Man Baptized a Third Time Just to Make Sure
SEMINOLE, TX

This past Sunday, Charles Peters, 32, of Seminole gained Ana-anabaptist status after undergoing his third baptism out of concern that the other two just weren't quite good enough to get him past the Pearly Gates when the time comes.

"It's not just anybody that gets official Ana-anabaptist certification," said Peters as he dried his hair with a towel. "I really don't know why it's not more common. I mean, they call us 're-baptizers' for a reason. I like to have it done once a decade or so. It's like renewing your vows."

Rarely seen in Mennonite circles, Peters says he also has a penchant for bodily cleanliness and takes a shower once a month whether he needs it or not, as any longer than that and he feels "icky." Baptism, he says, is similar.

"The first time I was 10, and then I hit puberty, and, well, you know how that goes ... After my teenage years, I needed to get washed again," explained Peters. "Then I went to college, read a little too much Kant, drank a beer or two, and, well, after all that it was time to do it again."

His next baptism is scheduled for the year 2026, at which point he will become an Ana-ana-anabaptist and officially break the record for the most baptized man on the planet.

LGBT Church Opens Doors in Southeastern Manitoba
LANDMARK, MB

A small Mennonite town in southeastern Manitoba has become home to the first LGBT church in the region. Landmark Gospel Brethren Tabernacle opened its doors in April and, according to senior pastor Menno Wiens, the fledgling congregation has already seen considerable growth.

"It's been a shock, really," said Wiens. "You don't expect to have a packed building every Sunday when you first start out, but the response has been tremendous. We're attracting people from all over, not just Landmark. Some folks are even coming in from the city."

The pastor at LGBT, which meets in a local farm implements dealership, notes that the new parishioners seem friendly.

"A lot of really nice people," said Wiens. "Two young women drove in from the city together. They even brought along what they called a 'pride flag,' which I think is great. We all should be proud to be believers."

The non-denominational church had considered joining the Quakers, but ultimately decided against it.

"I have a strong affinity for our theological cousins the Quakers," Wiens said. "I even made a church logo—LGBTQ—but in the end, we felt the Lord was leading us to go out on our own, so LGBT it was."

Despite the tremendous success of the church, Wiens sees further growth in the future.

"Outreach is very important," explained Wiens. "We want people to know that God loves everyone, not just those of us here in the LGBT community."

The church meets each Sunday morning at 10:30. LGBT Sunday school begins at 9:00.

Mennonite Woman Shunned for Marrying Outside Her Precise Denominational Affiliation
BERGTHAL, MB

Long-time CMMC member Esther Brandt was shunned by her community and church this past week for marrying Johan Fast, an EMMCer.

"She married outside the faith," explained CMMC pastor William Hiebert. "I mean, those EMMCers use a full three ounces more water in their baptisms, which is something we simply cannot abide. If Esther chooses to associate with such people, well, then we just cannot associate with her."

In 1925, with the influx of MBers into the area, the EMMB joined with the CMCMCC to become the CMMC and they have not spoken to each other ever since, especially because the former CMCMCCers later moved to Mexico to form the MCMCMCC conference, and the EMMBs who remain in the CMCMCC are seriously contemplating joining the M&Ms.

"She is now unequally yoked with an EMMCer, but at least she didn't marry a GCMBer. That would be even worse," said Hiebert. "The only church worse than them is the MBBM. Those people are just not right."

Now that they're married, Brandt and Fast plan to attend the local FEMB church, but they're also considering the BMs, BMBs, MBBs, MCCs, E=MCs … and the Lutherans.

Mennonite Man Can't Figure Out What to Give Up for Lent Since Everything Fun Is Already Forbidden
AKRON, PA

Mennonites across North America were baffled this week as other Christians were doing something called "Lent" for 40 days.

"Apparently they refrain from pleasure for 40 days," said Andrew Hostetler of Akron. "What would I give up? I'm already not doing anything fun."

The local Mennonite church already forbids smoking, dancing, drinking, and the use of modern technology, so Hostetler wasn't sure how this whole Lent thing was supposed to go down.

"So these other folks just have to be miserable for 40 days?" wondered Hostetler. "That seems a little slack. Us Mennonites have Lent 365 days a year!"

Hostetler suggested that if all these Lent-practising Christians wanted a real sacrifice, they could come haul manure on his pig farm for a few years.

"Being constrained to the regular Mennonite rules all year round is bad enough," said Hostetler, "and there are new rules all the time. The elders banned queen-sized beds just last month. That double bed gets pretty cramped for a family of eight."

Hostetler is considering converting to Catholicism just so he can have the pleasure of giving up booze and smoking for only one month a year.

Bible Camp Shuts Down After No One Memorizes Enough Verses to Attend

LITTLE HAPPY MENNO BIBLE CAMP, ON

Little Happy Menno Bible Camp in northern Ontario has had to shut its doors this summer after not enough kids memorized their verses this year.

"We kept lowering the minimum standard. Fifty verses equals one week at camp. Then 30, then 10. You need five verses to get a free bag of Old Dutch rapple chaps at the tuck shop, but lately they're not even memorizing that," said camp co-ordinator Bethany Stoesz. "These days we're lucky if they know John 3:16."

Stoesz suspects that "those new PlayStations" have something to do with the decline in verse memorization, but hopes things will pick up in the fall.

"Our Bible camp receives all its funding and support from verse memorization," said Stoesz. "We can't even fuel the generators until a few kids recite Psalm 23."

Local Sunday school teachers will be working hard in the off-season to get kids memorizing those verses so that Little Happy Menno Bible Camp can open again next year.

"We've had to sell off three canoes and a raft," said Stoesz, "but, Lord willing, we'll be back in business once the home-schooled kids contribute their verses."

Pastor Drops 5 Infants in Single Child Dedication Service
MOUNTAIN LAKE, MN

A reverend of a local Mennonite church has been sent on sabbatical this week after accidentally dropping nearly half a dozen infants in a single child dedication service.

"That Bentley Hiebert is a slippery little scamp," chuckled Rev. Kroeker. "It's a good thing his mom has quick reflexes."

After praying for young Bentley and dedicating his parents and the community to raising him up as a child of the King, the six-month-old slithered out of the pastor's hands as the congregation stood to affirm their commitment to lead godly lives as a model for the child.

"As Anabaptists, we don't believe in baptizing infants," said Kroeker. "Still, I feel someone must have got to these kids ahead of time and lathered them up with some kind of liquid."

After Bentley was dropped, the next couple reluctantly handed their young daughter Ashlynn to the jittery minister.

"We were pretty sure it wouldn't happen again," remarked Ashlynn's mother, "but alas, it did."

Even so, the Braun family, who were up next, handed their two young children, Elijah and Lacy, to the pastor, having full faith in their minister's ability to hold them in his trembling arms.

"I remember thinking, 'Hey, well, what are the odds that another child gets dropped?'" recalled Susan Braun. "He had one in each arm. He couldn't possibly drop them both."

The pastor prayed for safety and protection for the children, and promptly lost his grip, sending the poor babes plummeting to the carpet below.

Last up was little Cameron Goertzen, swaddled in a purple and gold Minnesota Vikings onesie.

"I had my eyes open the whole time we were praying," said Cameron's father, "and I could see my son slowly sliding down the pastor's torso. Cameron was clinging on by just a toe before I stepped in to rescue him."

Finally, the Associate Pastor intervened.

"I just figured enough was enough," said Associate Pastor Schultz. "How many children need to be dropped before the foam mattress is brought out?"

Fortunately, due to a well-padded sanctuary floor, none of the children were seriously injured, and the offering plates were passed from person to person without a hitch.

Steinbach Residents Flock to Mini-Churches Across the City
STEINBACH, MB

It's called the Tiny Church Movement, and it's taking the nation by storm. In Steinbach, Manitoba, area residents are abandoning the large megachurches in favour of something a little more intimate.

"We're getting back to the basics," said Janette Bergmann, local mom and mini-churchgoer. "Bigger isn't always better."

Bergmann meets with her two children, Lisa, 7, and Benjamin, 3, every Sunday morning in her own living room. Sometimes her husband Jason gets out of bed to join them.

"He's not the most committed mini-churchgoer," said Bergmann, "but sometimes he stops by for a quick prayer on his way to the bathroom."

Tiny churches like Bergmann's are cropping up all over Steinbach. Tired of the flash and pizzazz of ever-expanding stadium-sized churches, residents are preferring the contemplative mood of listening to "10,000 Reasons" between episodes of *Thomas the Tank Engine* and *Paw Patrol.*

"Who needs pyrotechnics when you have Netflix?" asked Bergmann, who is now calling herself Associate Pastor at 1625 Kroeker Avenue Mennonite Church.

Her Kroeker Avenue home is currently undergoing a massive redevelopment to accommodate the congregation.

"We are thinking of repainting the master bedroom and getting new linoleum in the kitchen," said Bergmann, "but I'm not sure that will be enough. When the twins are born, we may have to branch off and form a second church. Any more than three or four people and it just gets too impersonal. I mean, I haven't spoken with Pastor Jason in years. I don't even think he knows my name."

In response to the growth of mini-churches, established area megachurches are halting all construction projects until the wayward souls come back into the fold.

Mennonite Woman Dies After Serving on One Too Many Church Committees

ELKHART, IN

Local woman Mrs. Dorothy Shenk, 71, passed away this week after being asked to serve on yet another church committee. Before her untimely death by committee, Mrs. Shenk was happily serving on the South Elkhart Mennonite Church's Pulpit, Missions, Stewardship, Finance, Nominating, Music, Deacons, Trustees, Fellowship, Congregational Care, Outreach, Building, Gift Discernment, Wellness, Shoofly Pie, Feasibility, History, Diaper-Pinning, Special Function, Gymnasium, Peace and Social Justice, and Library committees, and the Committee Responsible for Forming Other Committees committee.

"She was gladly serving the Lord for decades, never turning down an opportunity to sit around a table drinking coffee and accomplishing nothing," said friend and fellow South Elkhart member Mrs. Roth. "It was all going well until she was asked to serve on the Christian Education committee. That's what finally did her in, I think."

The South Elkhart Mourning committee was quick to take charge of the situation and make arrangements for the funeral, while the Maintain the Status Quo committee took steps to ensure that this sort of thing is bound to happen again.

"We don't want Mrs. Shenk to have died in vain," said Public Relations committee leader Mr. Troyer. "That's why we've formed a new Mrs. Shenk Commemoration committee and a nine-member Everything Happens for a Reason committee to reassure the congregation."

The Committee-Forming committee did not immediately approve the application from a fringe group of South Elkharters to form a Committee to End Committees committee, but said they would discuss it at the next committee meeting.

Since passing away, Mrs. Shenk plans to volunteer on as many heavenly committees as is humanly possible, including the Keep the Streets Paved with Gold committee and the Keep the Lutherans Out committee.

Mennonite Man Excommunicated for Switching to John Deere

WARMAN, SK

Local flax grower Dwight Barkman, 47, was excommunicated from the MEMC Church this past Sunday after he refused to submit to church authority and replace his John Deere tractor with a Massey Ferguson.

"We here at the MEMC church believe that the Massey is the only truly righteous tractor," explained church elder Dick Unrau. "The John Deere is far too worldly and not nearly reliable enough. That's why all the MMBs across the street use it."

Barkman claimed he had been unaware the church had such a hardline stance against John Deere tractors and said that he could not afford to make the switch.

"I've already made five payments on the John Deere," said Barkman. "Plus, the elders have not been able to show sufficient scriptural support for their anti-Deere position."

The church elders claimed the Bible speaks very clearly against people like Barkman who just choose to "go their own way," and after three or four minutes of deliberation, decided to excommunicate Barkman and his entire family.

"I guess we'll go to the MMB church," said Barkman. "It's a caring congregation where they allow anyone in, regardless of the brand of tractor you happen to drive."

Barkman later discovered the MMB church has a very strong tradition of growing canola and that he, a flax farmer, was not welcome there either.

New *Mennonite Hymnal* Eliminates Verse 3 From Every Hymn

HARRISONBURG, VA

A brand-new edition of the classic *Mennonite Hymnal* has been slimmed down a little with the elimination of verse three from every single hymn.

"No one was singing verse three anyway," said hymnal editor Tiffany Good. "It was always, 'Women on verse one, just the men on verse two, skip verse three, then everyone altogether on verse four.' That's the way Mennonites have sung hymns for centuries."

It is thought by Mennonite church music historians that verse three was shunned sometime in the 1700s for dressing immodestly.

"We don't have any clear record on why verse three was shunned," said historian Peter Yoder, "but we do know that verse three was asked to apologize in front of the congregation and refused. Since then, Mennonites have had nothing to do with any verse three they've come across."

In reaction to these changes, some more liberal Mennonite congregations have created their own hymnal consisting of nothing but verse threes.

Man Escapes Mennonite Section of Heaven, Is Shocked at What He Finds

HEAVEN

Mr. Abe Penner of Earth passed away in January 1968 and, for almost 50 years, had been living a quiet, peaceful existence in the Mennonite section of Heaven, blissfully unaware of the vast expanse of Paradise that lay just beyond the border.

"I have to admit, when I first got here, Heaven was a lot smaller than I expected and I was surprised everyone spoke Plautdietsch," explained Penner. "Quite frankly, it's a lot like home, but the housebarns are much larger and there aren't any elders around to tell us what to do."

Everything changed for Mr. Penner this past week when a paperwork mix-up had him transferred to the Catholic section.

"What the heck is this place and who are these people?" wondered Mr. Penner as he sauntered past mansions filled with people who baptize babies. "*Oba nä!* If I had known they'd be letting Catholics in here I'd have been a lot less uptight about the drinking and dancing while I was alive."

Penner was shocked by the diversity of doctrine in Paradise, saying that Heaven was nothing at all like he expected.

"It's as if all that fighting over theology back on Earth was a complete waste of time or something," said Penner. "I mean, when I look around me, I'm pretty sure our pastor back home didn't get a single thing right."

Mr. Penner has decided to stay in the Catholic section of Heaven for the rest of eternity, or at least until some of his grandchildren pass and he finally has someone he can beat in a game of *kjnipsbrat.*

The Seven Deadly Sins (for Mennonites)

While many are familiar with the Roman Catholic list of seven deadly sins (i.e., sloth, gluttony, and so on), fewer people are aware that us Mennonites have seven lethal sins of our own. The list was compiled by Menno Simons and Conrad Grebel at a meeting in a Zurich pub back in 1526 and has been the foundation for Mennonite morality and ethics ever since.

1. Failure to finish Oma's *plautz*. Mennonites are not against gluttony. In fact, we highly encourage it. When you're at Oma's house and she points out, after the third helping of *plautz* or *vereniki* or whatever it is, that "there's more, *jung*, there's more," you are obliged to consume every last perogy. Anything less is a grave violation of this basic principle. Finish your food or expect the wrath of Grandma and the elders.

2. Having a small family. Mennonites encourage copious intimate behaviour between married couples. As long as the goal is procreation, you can come together as often as you like. A minimum of 12 children is required or all that recreation will be classified as "fornication."

3. Insufficient pride about your humility. While the Catholic list outright prohibits pride, the Mennonite list actually encourages it in a roundabout way. There is one thing, and one thing alone, that Mennonites can be proud of, and that is your utter lack of pride.

4. Greed (without tithing). While many Mennonites in recent decades have accumulated massive quantities of personal wealth, hoarding money is only considered "greed" if your tithes are not large enough. Pay for a new church gymnasium and you can live it up in the Cayman Islands all you want.

5. Envying your neighbour's cattle. There's an old Mennonite saying: "Be content with your cow, your mare, and your sow." The Lord, and possibly the Credit Union, has entrusted you with your cattle, whether a small herd or large. Be good stewards of your livestock and keep your eyes on your own udders.

6. Getting angry (at something other than ice hockey). Mennonites are taught to hold all our anger inside until it manifests itself as unhealthy passive-aggressive behaviour. Under no circumstances can we resort to violence. The only exceptions are at the EMC hockey tournament or the annual MB crokinole competition.

7. Being lazy around harvest time. Mennonites work hard—not to accumulate wealth, but to stay out of trouble and get the grain in the elevator. The only instance in which sloth is acceptable is if you're ever asked to dance. In that case, you must politely reply "no thanks" and let that Englisher assume you're just too lazy to get up on your feet.

Unmarried Couple Caught Holding Hymnal Together
FRESNO, CA

An unmarried couple at South Fresno Mennonite Church are facing intense scrutiny after they were caught grasping opposite corners of the same hymnal during a rousing rendition of "Blessed Assurance" this past Sunday. The church takes cases of overt lewdness like this very seriously and has called upon the couple to explain themselves.

"Sharing hymnals before marriage is a very serious offence," said Elder Johan. "It's bad enough that we let them sit near each other, but now they're even singing from the same hymn book? Disgusting!"

One of the accused, Miss Helena Fehr, 20, says she never intended to grasp hold of Peter Ginter's hymnal, but that when he saw her looking around for a book, he offered to share his.

"I don't know what came over me. I just reached out and grabbed the edge," said Fehr. "He didn't seem to mind. He didn't pull away or anything. So we just sang like that with our hands on the same hymnal until the end of all five verses."

After hearing the couple's pleas for mercy, the elder board decided the only right thing to do in a situation like this is for the couple to get married as soon as possible.

"I was really hoping to hold hymnals with a few more young men before I got hitched," said Fehr, "but it looks like I'll have to be content with holding Peter Ginter's hymnal for the rest of my life."

Peter Ginter says he is happy to be marrying Helena, as he was sick and tired of holding his own hymnal all these years.

Mennonite Woman Concerned She Might Be Anglican
WINNIPEG, MB

A Mennonite woman from Winnipeg has been wondering lately whether it just might be that she's actually an Anglican. Miss Hailey Enns, 23, started having Anglican thoughts a few years ago and has even attended a service or two.

"I don't know what it is, but I tend to gravitate towards the liturgical," said Enns. "There are times when I just feel like going up to the front and drinking communion from a communal goblet rather than sitting around waiting for Mr. Klassen to hand out the tiny plastic cups."

Enns says it took her a long time to work up the courage to tell her parents, who are committed members at Northwest Kildonan EMBC church.

"I knew what they'd say. 'Who's gonna make *faspa* if you're an Anglican?' or, 'What kind of example are you setting for your future children?' but that just doesn't change how I feel," said Enns. "To me, I'd much rather worship the Lord sitting beneath a beautiful stained-glass window than crammed next to Mrs. Doerksen in the women's section."

Some of Enns's friends have been supportive of her journey, but her father, Ken, is really shook up over it.

"It's like one day she's all about Menno Simons and the next it's all Henry VIII. I can't figure it out," said Ken. "All I can hope is that she doesn't find some Anglican boy or all my grandkids will wind up Armstrongs or Smiths or something."

Enns says she's almost ready to join the Church of England if only she can figure out some way to go back in time 23 years and be baptized as an infant.

Naive Young Man Still Hoping to Meet Eligible Young Woman in Church

YARROW, BC

Local bachelor Anthony Hamm, 24, of Yarrow is sticking to his guns and showing up to church every Sunday hoping and praying that a young woman his age will miraculously appear. Hamm has been an active member of West Yarrow GCMB since he was a child but is starting to lose his patience.

"Don't get me wrong, I love seniors," said Hamm, "but just once I'd love to see a single young woman in skinny jeans sitting across the aisle from me and passing the offering plate."

Hamm is West Yarrow's token young person and the seniors are desperate to keep him around.

"I keep telling him, 'Oh, don't you worry, Anthony. Someday your princess will come. Just wait and see what the Lord has in store for you!'" said Mrs. Hildebrandt. "I'm not really so optimistic, but I want him to keep attending our church. He's the only one who knows how to operate the overhead projector."

Occasionally, Mrs. Hildebrandt will invite her granddaughter Stephanie to church, just to give young Anthony some hope.

"Stephanie's engaged to some guy from Germany," said Mrs. Hildebrandt, "but I bring her around anyway. It keeps Anthony interested in church."

Anthony recently announced that if he's not engaged by the end of the summer, he's going to try his luck on Plenty of Fish.

Mennonite Church Allows Dancing Now That Everyone Has to Keep 6 Feet Apart

SWIFT CURRENT, SK

The COVID-19 pandemic has led to a lot of strange behaviour, such that even the strictest of Mennonite churches have decided to relax the rules when it comes to dancing. Pastor Tom of Swift Current has decreed that since everyone has to keep six feet apart these days anyway, they might as well be allowed a little rhythmic movement.

"As long as I can shove two crokinole boards between you, it shouldn't be a problem," said Pastor Tom. "You can Lindy Hop and jitterbug all you want at that distance."

Pastor Tom is even planning Swift Current's first-ever church dance this Saturday in the large *faspa* room downstairs.

"We'll crank up the Glenn Miller and let 'er rip," said Pastor Tom. "I think it'll be our most popular youth event since the jam-making workshop last fall."

Despite the new relaxed view regarding dancing, Pastor Tom says that the physical distancing rules will still be strictly enforced.

"I don't care if you think that handsome young man across the room is your second cousin on your mother's side," said Pastor Tom. "You ain't getting close enough to find out."

Tickets to the dance also include an all-you-can-eat dill pickle buffet, but Mrs. Reimer, chair of the *faspa* committee, assured health officials that all the dills will be spaced a full two metres apart.

90% of Heavy Metal Bands Fronted by Pastors' Sons
ST. JACOBS, ON

A new study conducted at Woolwich Township University reveals that the vast majority of heavy and/or death metal bands are fronted by the sons of pastors, frequently of Mennonite or Baptist persuasion.

"It's startling, really," said Professor Hannah Martin. "I mean, we all know about a pastor's son or two who went off the deep end, but apparently the phenomenon is a lot more common than any of us could have imagined."

From Iron Maiden and Judas Priest to Slayer and Anthrax, pastors' sons just seem to be attracted to heavy metal music for some reason.

"I was really surprised to discover that everyone in Iron Maiden, other than the drummer, is a pastor's son," said Martin. "And Black Sabbath? Well, all those guys were raised in the homes of Anglican vicars."

The news came as no surprise to St. Jacobs youth pastor Darryl Wenger, however.

"I've seen every single one of Reverend Brubacher's sons come and go through my youth group," said Wenger. "They'd start in grade seven as perfect little Sunday school students. Then it's an earring and smoking cigarettes behind the parsonage, then they're wearing fewer and fewer white-collared shirts and more tattered black T-shirts, and the next thing you know they're covering Pantera songs and drinking light beer in the garage."

The study also revealed that almost all of the raunchiest pop singers are pastors' daughters.

Mennonite Couple Comes Late to Church and Has to Settle for Front Row

HERBERT, SK

The Driedgers of Herbert, Saskatchewan had a pretty hectic morning this Sunday when the toaster didn't work, the hot water tank died, and they just had to squeeze in a quick *meddachschlop* right before church. Needless to say, the couple was an embarrassing 15 minutes late for church and had to settle for one of the first three rows.

"*Oba*, they're singing already. Where on earth are we going to sit?" said Mrs. Driedger, still composing herself after a particularly vigorous *meddachschlop*. "All the seats are taken!"

Oh, but they weren't all taken. In what has been described as the "greatest travesty in Herbert Mennonite Church history," the Driedgers found that the only empty pews were right in the front.

"No one likes to sit too close to the pastor," said Mr. Driedger. "He tends to spit when he talks."

Still, the Driedgers had no other choice and reluctantly plopped themselves down in the first pew, much to the horror of the congregation.

"I wish them all the best way up there in the front," said Mrs. Petkau in row 17. "I've never ventured closer than row five myself. All I have to say to the Driedgers is good luck and God bless!"

The Driedgers managed to survive the entire service up there in the front, but the experience was so unpleasant that they vowed to be extra early next Sunday.

"Or else we'll just wedge ourselves next to the Unger family," said Mrs. Driedger. "They always seem to have plenty of room."

The Driedgers have also considered bribing one of the ushers for a prime spot in the back, although the ethics of this has not yet been studied in the adult Sunday school class.

A Mennonite Guide to Earning Your Salvation

Newly discovered documents published by Dirk Philips in the mid-1500s have finally put to rest the age-old Mennonite question of how to go about earning your place in Heaven. While Calvinists believe that some people are "predestined" to go to Heaven, Mennonites have been a little less certain about the topic and feel there are things you can do to have a better chance of getting in there. As flawed as this theology might be, perhaps this simple scoring system developed by the amateur Biblical scholars at *The Daily Bonnet* will provide some struggling souls with solace.

1. Attending church every single Sunday for 80 years—100 points

2. Missing a Sunday—minus 20 points for each Sunday missed

3. Attending Sunday evening services without complaining—30 points

4. Complaining about attending evening services —minus 5 points for each occurrence

5. Dressing modestly (Mrs. Wall's definition of "modest")—100 points

6. Dressing modestly (Emma Goertzen's definition) —minus 30 points

7. Perfect Sunday school attendance—60 points

8. Teaching Sunday school—50 points (100 points if you had the Reimer twins in your class)

9. Speaking fluent Plautdietsch or Pennsylvania German/Dutch—75 points

10. Knowing only the swears—30 points

11. Uttering one of those swears—minus 5 points for each occurrence

12. Memorizing the Sermon on the Mount—50 points

13. Living it—1,000 points

14. Being baptized sometime during your teen years—50 points

15. Being baptized in your early 20s just so you can get married—20 points

16. Being baptized as an infant—minus 100 points

17. Going on a missions trip—50 points for each trip (maximum 500 points)

18. Going on a missions trip from Winkler to Morden—20 points for each trip (maximum 100 points)

19. Paying for someone else's missions trip—10 points for each occurrence (maximum 100 points)

20. Praying for someone else's missions trip—5 points for each occurrence (maximum 50 points)

21. Praying against missions trips you don't believe in—5 points for each occurrence (maximum 50 points)

22. Serving as a Conscientious Objector during a major military conflict—200 points

23. Claiming to be a pacifist from the convenience and comfort of a modern democratic nation that doesn't require you to kill anyone—3 points

24. Giving money to the poor—1 point for every $100 given (maximum 100 points)

25. Stealing money from the offering plate—minus 100 points for every $1 taken

26. Stealing money from the offering plate and giving it to the poor—neutral

27. Visiting elderly relatives in the hospital—10 points for each occurrence (maximum of 100 points)

28. Bathing elderly relatives in the hospital—20 points for each occurrence (maximum of 200 points)

29. Converting a heathen—100 points

30. Heathening a convert—minus 100 points

Points required to guarantee a spot in Heaven: 7,777

Gossip Masquerades as 'Prayer Request' Yet Again This Sunday
GOESSEL, KS

Mr. Erwin Unruh stood up, once again, this Sunday to request prayer for his next-door neighbours, Mr. and Mrs. William and Susanna Warkentin, whom he overheard yelling.

"You know what I heard?" said Mr. Unruh. "Those fighting Warkentins ... and right in front of their children yet. It was completely unseemly. Not to mention that their adult daughter Rebecca has moved to the city. I hear she's just not right with the Lord."

Unruh went on for about five minutes explaining all the things he had heard in the coffee shop about the Warkentins' marital troubles.

"So, they could really use our prayers," concluded Mr. Unruh. "And don't get me started about those Funks. Now that's a family that could use some divine intervention, let me tell you. Did you hear that ..."

Unruh continued his "prayer request" while the congregation jotted down everything they heard in little notebooks so that they could "pray more effectively during the week." After a while, Mrs. Bartel interjected.

"What was the Warkentins' daughter's name again?" she asked, scribbling notes for posterity. "Right, right, thanks, got it."

Bartel was really excited about all the detailed material she gathered for the upcoming prayer meeting on Thursday.

"That Mr. Unruh is a treasure trove of juicy prayer requests," said Mrs. Bartel. "It's going to be quite a long prayer meeting this week. I hope we can finally find out what happened to Mrs. Warkentin on that recent so-called 'shopping trip,' if you can believe that. I'm on the edge of my seat in anticipation. I'm sure the Lord is too."

Mennonite Church Signs Pastor to Massive 30-Year $1.2 Million Contract

MORDEN, MB

Dave Hiebert, 28, the hottest free-agent pastor on the market, has just inked a 30-year contract extension with West Morden Mennonite Church. The new record-setting contract is reportedly worth close to $1.2 million spread out over the next three decades and includes a signing bonus of a gift card to The Keg.

"We're happy to have Pastor Dave locked up until 2047," explained church president Bill Falk. "Pastor Dave brings a lot to the table and we're really excited to see his smiling face every single Sunday for the next 30 years."

The contract is both the longest and most lucrative ever signed by a Mennonite pastor, and West Morden Mennonite Church members are excited to have Hiebert at the helm of a pastoral team that also includes a half-time youth pastor and a quarter-time secretary making $8.50/hour.

"From now on, we're calling him the Million Dollar Pastor," said Falk. "I just hope all this money doesn't go to his head. I also know we're all praying he doesn't get a career-ending concussion in year two of the contract or something."

Pastor Dave says he's really excited to be lacing up his skates for West Morden again, and now that contract negotiations have ended, he plans to spend more time on sermon preparation.

"I've got a really awesome 15-part series coming up on the Book of Zephaniah," he said. "I hope I'll have time to slip in that visit to The Keg ... thanks for the $20 gift card!"

3 Mennonites Hospitalized After Brutal Drive-By Shunning

KIDRON, OH

Three young Mennonites are convalescing in the church basement this evening after being rudely ignored by several acquaintances at a Kidron-area Walmart earlier in the day.

"We're not yet sure what prompted the shunning," said Officer Martin Kraybill. "As far as we can tell, it was random. The shunners came armed with furrowed brows and mercilessly judgmental attitudes."

Reports indicate the shunning took place in the vegetable aisle near the russet potatoes, where the shunners simply walked right past their fellow Mennonites without even a friendly hello or anything.

"I get it, you're at Walmart, and that can make anyone cranky," said Kraybill, "but that's no excuse for a shunning. Just be grateful you're not stuck in line at Costco on a Saturday."

Kidron police claim they have two suspects in custody, but a third perpetrator managed to evade arrest after a high-speed horse-and-buggy chase, and is still at large. The public is warned not to make contact with the suspect, as he is considered armed with a wide-brimmed hat and a really dangerous frowny face.

Mennonite Church Sets Record by Standing Up and Sitting Down More than 600 Times in a Single Service
NIAGARA-ON-THE-LAKE, ON

The Eastside Niagara-on-the-Lake Mennonite Church set a world record this Sunday after Pastor Ron had the congregation stand up, sit down, and stand up again more than 600 times in a single service.

"We honestly weren't going for any record," said Pastor Ron. "It's just that we had a lot of responsive readings and prayers … and the fact we ended up at 606 is just icing on the cake."

The congregation first stood up to greet each other, then sat down for the responsive reading, then stood up again for a boisterous singing of "Life Is Like a Mountain Railroad," and then sat down again while the Heinrichs sisters performed a skit based on Jonah 2:10, then up again for the prayer, then down again for the children's story, then up again for "True Evangelical Faith," then down again for the more sombre "Peace in the Valley," and up and down like this another 598 times.

"To be honest, I didn't even notice we were approaching a record until about halfway through the service when Mrs. Peters tapped me on the shoulder and told me to keep it up because we were on pace to shatter the Elmira record of 504 ups and downs back in '97," said Pastor Ron. "At that point, I was just hoping no one's back would give out."

Exhilarated after the service, church member Mrs. Kornelsen, 76, claims she feels ready to run the Niagara Marathon.

"I haven't done that many deep knee bends in ages," said Kornelsen, dripping with sweat. "It's nice being able to learn a little from the Word and get in a full-body workout at the same time!"

After the wild success of the service, Pastor Ron is thinking of installing a couple hundred stationary bikes in the sanctuary and running spin classes every Sunday morning.

Church With 250 Members Splits Into 250 Churches
LANCASTER, PA

After a particularly heated membership meeting this past week, the South Lancaster Mennonite Church has decided to split the entire congregation into more manageable units of one.

"At first we decided to just split into two groups: those in favour of buttons on their shirts and those who prefer hooks," explained Daniel B. Miller, former South Lancaster elder and recently appointed pastor of Daniel B. Miller Memorial Church, "but then the button-users started talking amongst themselves and found they had differences of opinion on baptismal water temperature. Those wanting hot and those wanting cold split into their own groups. So then we had pro-button pro-cold, pro-button anti-cold, anti-button pro-cold and anti-button anti-cold groups. I figured it was settled, but upon further discussion, the groups realized they couldn't agree on whether to sing five or six hymns each Sunday, and so there was an anti-button-anti-cold-pro-five group and an anti-button-anti-cold-pro-six group, and a pro-button-anti-cold-pro-five group and … well, you get the idea. The groups just kept getting smaller and smaller. Eventually we all decided to each form our own churches … but there was some opposition to that idea too."

The once-thriving South Lancaster Church is now 250 (253, to be precise) individual churches, although the division continues.

"This whole starting-your-own-church thing has got me studying theology," explained Miller, "and now I change church doctrine every day. I don't even agree with myself anymore!"

Miller says he has excommunicated his past self for

differences on clerical celibacy but is concerned that a future version of himself might disagree.

"Who knows what I might believe this Friday afternoon," explained Miller. "I always get a little too liberal when the weekend approaches. Being my own pastor is a lot harder than I thought. You get so much criticism from all sides and it's almost impossible to get everyone to agree."

Pastor Daniel is arranging an ecumenical reconciliation service between his various selves for Sunday morning … although he can't figure out whether they should use real wine or just Welch's grape juice.

Stars of *Hymn Sing:* Where Are They Now?
WINNIPEG, MB

Every Sunday afternoon for more than 30 years, Winnipeg singers delighted audiences on the hit CBC television show *Hymn Sing*. It should not be surprising that many former *Hymn Sing* members have gone on to do great things. We've caught up with a few of them to find out about their post-*Hymn-Sing* lives.

- Barney Loewen (active from 1972 to 1983): "Once I left *Hymn Sing*, my life was a mess. I tried to salvage a music career after that, even taught piano lessons for a while, but eventually I got involved in the Winnipeg underground punk rock scene. I played lead guitar for a band called the Depraved Mennos. You may have heard of us. Our LP is a collector's item now. It's so rare, I don't even have a copy myself. Can anyone hook me up with one?"

- Allen Giesbrecht (active from 1965 to 1967): "I was Altona's first-ever Rhodes Scholar and *Hymn Sing* member. I don't know which accomplishment I'm prouder of. I did a PhD in economics, but I could never apply what I learned to my own life. I've got major financial problems now. I don't really want to get into it. My only happy memories are from my time on *Hymn Sing*."

- Samantha Plett (active from 1989 to 1991): "I'm a former Treble Teen who made it onto *Hymn Sing*. I like to show my children some of my old *Hymn Sing* episodes, but if it doesn't have Beyoncé or Jay-Z in it, they're just not interested. It's too bad. We did a truly amazing version of the 'Old Rugged Cross.' That was probably my favourite."

- Simon Hildebrandt (active from 1981 to 1982):"I was only on *Hymn Sing* for about six months before quitting the show to run for office as a member of the Marxist-Leninist Party. I wasn't elected, but I did get close to 30 votes, so I'm pretty proud of that accomplishment. I'm now a blogger."

- Marnie Vogt (active from 1991 to 1995):"I met my first three husbands on *Hymn Sing*: Peter, Paul, and Bennie. After three nasty divorces, from which I had to relinquish half my *Hymn Sing* wealth to my no-good husbands, I gave up on hymn singers and, after two more tries, I am now happily married to a pastor's son."

Fists Fly After Loewen Family Sits in Penner Family Pew
LA CRETE, AB

Fifteen members of the Loewen family and 23 Penners were hospitalized this past week after a brawl broke out at the local Mennonite church. The brawl seems to have been initiated after four members of the Loewen family decided to "change it up a little" and sit in the Penner family pew.

"I didn't see their name on it," said Doug Loewen, who was released from the hospital after receiving 14 stitches for a laceration above his eye. "I was under the impression it was first come, first served when it comes to church seating."

Terry Penner, now suffering from concussion symptoms, saw things a little differently.

"The Penners have been sitting in row three since 1981," said Penner, "and don't let Doug fool you. He knows it's our pew."

Terry was reportedly less than polite in asking the Loewen family to move, to which Doug responded with a shove to the chest. That shove, known as "the shot heard round La Crete," started an all-out brawl, which drew in Penners and Loewens from all over the sanctuary.

"It was absolute mayhem. Blood. Fists. Plenty of language unsuitable for church," explained one observer. "I guess it's true: around here, we take church pews very seriously."

After calming the angry crowd with watermelon and *roll kuchen,* Pastor Ron took to the pulpit to address the church.

"Friends, in order to maintain harmonious relationships and restore the congregation's commitment to peace and charity," said Pastor Ron in a stirring and heartfelt sermon, "there must be no more discussions about changing spots in the sanctuary. This madness must end!"

Spurred on by Pastor Ron's words, the elder board held a quick vote confirming the pastor's message and officially decreed that all families must sit in the very same seats they've used for the past three decades.

New Edition of *Martyrs Mirror* to Include Section on Minor Inconveniences Facing the Modern North American Church

COLUMBUS, OH

For centuries, Thieleman J. van Braght's *Martyrs Mirror* or *The Bloody Theater* has preserved the horrific stories of martyrdom faced by Christians of the past. Now, in the book's first update in more than 300 years, these tales of martyrs being burned at the stake will be joined by tales of the absolutely appalling conditions facing modern-day North American Christians, such as having to wear a thin paper mask during a pandemic or being stuck in the checkout line behind some dude buying lotto tickets.

"I'm really looking forward to the new 'Minor Inconveniences' section!" said one local churchgoer and persecution complex sufferer. "I can't wait to see Jan Luyken's copper engraving of me whining about the time I hit every single red light on the way to church. That's gotta go right next to the story of Dirk Willems!"

The newly expanded edition will include horrific atrocities facing North American Christians over the past 100 years, such as being richer than any other social group on the planet, with the possible exception of, like, Norwegians or something, the time the guy from *Duck Dynasty* was fired and then quickly unfired, and having to suffer through that terrible *Cats* movie.

"When I think of how my brothers and sisters around my wealthy suburban neighbourhood are suffering for their faith, it breaks my heart," said one local woman. "I mean, last week, Mrs. Schmidt was trying to watch the Sunday church service on her iPad when the Wi-Fi went out for a full 20 minutes and she missed half of Pastor Darryl's sermon. If that's not persecution, I can't imagine what is!"

Martyrs Mirror: Tales of the Minorly Inconvenienced will go on sale this month exclusively from Amazon.

Mennonite Brethren and General Conference Forced to Share Folklorama Pavilion

WINNIPEG, MB

Folklorama is an annual festival celebrating the multicultural mosaic of Manitoba. However, conflict erupted this year after organizers required Mennonite Brethren and Mennonite Church Canada (formerly General Conference) members to share the very same Mennonite Pavilion.

"There's no way I'm sharing a booth with one of those liberal General Conferencers!" shouted visibly distraught MB member Gladys Dueck, spear in hand. "How can anyone say we're the same culture?!"

Since emerging as two distinct groups in the 1860s, the MBs and MCs have distinguished themselves from each other in a variety of ways. Notable areas of difference include modes of baptism, some social issues, and the correct method for crimping perogies.

"Plus, we're much better singers," said Dueck. "You can't possibly expect me to share a hymnal with someone who can't tell an F sharp from a G flat!"

Efforts to share the pavilion resulted in intermittent gladiator-style fights throughout the evening, with equipment borrowed from the Italian Pavilion. After a few hours, and with many Mennonites sporting fractured ribs and missing teeth, both the MBs and MCs decided it "just wasn't working."

"There's a reason we can't share a church building," said General Conference member Karen Fehr, her arm in a sling. "It's the same reason we didn't even invite the EMCers at all. We actually agreed with the MBs on that one."

While some have pointed out that Mennonites, as a religious denomination and not a distinct culture, shouldn't even have a pavilion, others praised the efforts of the organizers to unite the two groups.

"I like it. Put all the Mennonites in the same pavilion," said Folklorama attendee Art Neustaedter. "I mean, Lord knows if we allowed every Mennonite group with some trivial theological difference to have their own spot there'd be a thousand different Mennonite pavilions here. One is more than enough, I say."

9-Pound Mennonite Baby Miraculously Born 3 Months Premature

ALTONA, MB

Just six months after Peter and Elvira Doerksen were married in the Altona MCMB church, the couple experienced the miraculous birth of their firstborn son, Timothy.

"We're really glad that he was a healthy weight, even though I was just at the end of my second trimester," said proud mother Elvira. "The pastor is calling it a miracle because there simply is no other explanation as to how young Timothy could be fully developed only six months after Peter and I were bound in holy matrimony."

This is not the first miraculous occurrence of its kind in Altona's history. The town has been blessed with the birth of five healthy zygotes this past year alone.

"It's just amazing," explained MCMB Pastor David R. Unrau. "Babies are being born earlier and earlier it seems. I just married Mr. and Mrs. Jack Hildebrand five weeks ago and they've already given birth to two bouncing baby embryos. Twins!"

The rapid rate of fetal development in Altona has mystified local physicians, who cannot explain how all these babies could be born less than nine months after their parents were married.

"It's scientifically impossible," said Dr. Peters, a longtime member of MCMB church. "The Lord truly works in mysterious ways."

Congregation Shocked as Guitarist Snaps a G String

HENDERSON, NE

Parishioners at the South Henderson Mennonite Church were in shock this last week after song leader and guitarist Joanne Voth lost her G string right in the middle of "Refiner's Fire."

"I've never seen anything like it. I mean, sure, I've seen the youth leader lose a C or even a high E, but never in all my years at this church have I seen a snapped G string," said attendee Judy Hamm. "Let me tell you, my Dietrich had to get out the smelling salts after witnessing that G string flying into the front row."

Miss Voth apologized for the errant G string and says she won't play the guitar quite so vigorously next time.

"There's a reason we mostly do hymns around here," said Voth. "Those contemporary praise and worship songs really do a number on your G string!"

Voth managed to replace her G string with a new one and was ready to go by the time the worship team started playing "Good Good Father."

"I've always got an extra G string with me in church," said Voth. "You never know when something like this is going to happen!"

The horrified response to the snapped G string at the Mennonite church stands in stark contrast to the evangelical church across the road, where snapping G strings are a much more common occurrence.

Mennonite Woman Feels Really Guilty
for Not Feeling Guilty Enough

AYLMER, ON

Days after a pleasant holiday season in which she was a gracious and generous host, a local Mennonite woman reports feeling "just really awful" about the fact that she feels good about herself.

"I was lying awake all night, worried about the fact I couldn't think of a single thing to feel guilty about," said Mrs. Helen J. Braun of Aylmer. "I can't remember the last time I had a clear conscience like this ... and it really bothers me."

Braun says she racked her brain trying to think of something she'd done wrong, whether it was a greedy thought, an impolite word, or a misplaced pickle, and couldn't think of anything at all.

"I liked it a lot better when I was sinning on occasion," said Braun. "Then at least I could find the source of my guilt. But this is driving me nuts. I just don't know what to do."

Braun reports telling her pastor about the problem. He informed her that this guilt is a natural consequence of her Mennonite upbringing ... and is nothing to feel guilty about.

Mennonite Publisher Releases Extra-Wide Bibles to Keep Boys and Girls Farther Apart

GOSHEN, IN

The Mennonite Bible Society of Indiana is excited to announce they will now be offering brand-new, extra-thick Bibles intended to provide additional distance between the young men and women at youth meetings, teen Sunday school classes, and other church functions.

"The width of the Bible has always been our measuring tool," said Vice President Walter Yoder, head of the Bible Thickness committee, "but we've been noticing a pattern of thinner and thinner Bibles out there. I don't know what they're leaving out, but it's sure making things difficult to manage at our campfire singalongs."

Yoder's Extra-Wide, as the new Bibles are called, are a full 10 inches thick and have been padded out with Yoder's detailed commentary below each verse, not that he's expecting anyone to actually read it.

"These Bibles are strictly for measurement purposes," said Yoder. "In fact, I recommend wedging two or three of them between the young people if things really get out of hand."

Yoder says the Bibles can also be used to make sure hemlines are an adequate distance below the knee.

"I'm confident these are the most versatile Bibles ever published," said Yoder. "You don't even have to crack them open and you'll be radically transformed."

Yoder's Extra-Wide Bibles are in stores now, just in time for the last two weeks of teen summer camp.

Missionaries Discover New Position
WINDHOEK, NAMIBIA

Curtis and Patricia Bueckert, who left Manitoba more than 20 years ago to serve as Bible translators in Namibia, have shattered many assumptions about missionaries after announcing plans to try out an exciting new position while they're on furlough this spring.

"It's new to us, anyway," said Patricia with a smile. "We had a lot of time to learn local customs when we weren't translating the Book of Acts. I had no idea there was a second position."

The Bueckerts say that when they found out about this new approach, they were initially hesitant to try it, especially while they were still on the mission field.

"When we signed up to be missionaries, we agreed to a lifestyle commitment that limited us to just the one position," said Patricia. "It says nothing about what we do on furlough, though, so I can't wait to get back to Morden!"

When they return to Canada, the Bueckerts plan to tour rural Manitoba and share what they've learned while away.

"I usually let Curtis do all the talking," said Patricia, "but this time I feel led to speak. It's really important for people back home in the Pembina Valley to hear our message of hope."

Most churches provide only a 20-minute time slot for missionary reports, but Patricia hopes that the time may be extended to accommodate her detailed slide show.

Choir Director Admits He Really Doesn't Know What the Heck He's Doing With His Arms

SASKATOON, SK

Mr. Allan Vogt, choir director at Third Mennonite Church in Saskatoon, admitted in a candid interview this past week that he's basically just standing up there and flailing his arms about randomly.

"It's all meaningless," confessed Vogt. "I move them up, I move them down, I pinch my fingers together. None of it means anything. The choir knows what to do ..."

Vogt has been known to occasionally turn around and attempt to direct the congregation in the singing of a hymn, but admits that this, too, is just an act.

"I've got no control over those people," said Vogt. "I mean, my arms go up and Mr. Reimer goes into falsetto. My arms go down and Mrs. Fehr sings the echo part. It's absolute chaos."

Vogt says he's taken a few moves from air traffic controllers; others he's learned while eavesdropping on his wife's yoga DVDs.

"I get inspiration from everywhere," said Vogt, "but let me tell you, I'm certain I'm not the only one up there faking it on Sunday morning."

Inspired by Vogt's candidness, Pastor Glen admitted that the vast majority of his Sunday morning pulpit-pounding is also just for show.

Mennonite Child Forced to Miss *Wonderful World of Disney* to Attend Evening Service

MITCHELL, MB

Collin Berg, 7, of Mitchell had to miss *The Wonderful World of Disney* yet again this weekend to attend the EMBC *faspa* and evening service.

"Now I'll never know what happens to the Apple Dumpling Gang!" sobbed young Collin. "This is as bad as last month when I only saw the second half of *Herbie Goes Bananas.*"

Collin's father, Earl, says there are more important things than finding out what happens on *Pete's Dragon* or *Snowball Express.*

"Besides, *Old Yeller* always has him in tears," said Earl, "and he's usually more than ready for a good night's sleep after one of Pastor Don's sermons and a few slices of marble cheese."

Collin is begging his dad to let him set the VCR to record *Flight of the Navigator* next week, but Earl says the VCR can only be used for high-quality children's programming like *Son of Flubber* and *The Shaggy D.A.*

Mennonite Man Refunded Tuition
After Graduating Bible School Single
ROSTHERN, SK

Tyler Peters, 22, was the lone unmarried graduate at Rosthern Bible Institute this spring and thus was refunded his full tuition including the cost of textbooks.

"Ugh, well, I guess I just wasted the last four years of my life," said Peters. "I never should have done that Honours degree."

Most students were paired up by the end of the first semester, but Peters kept on attending in hopes that maybe there would be a sophomore breakup he could swoop in on.

"But it never happened," said Peters. "They were all swapping their promise rings for engagement rings pretty quick. Even Gertie Fehr found a match. What's a Mennonite boy to do?"

Peters received a $32,000 cheque along with his diploma and a sincere apology from the chancellor of the school.

"We're always striving to do better," said RBI Chancellor Bergman, "but sometimes it's just a numbers game and someone's gonna be left out. I wish Tyler nothing but the best as he soldiers on looking for that special someone at his church College and Career group."

Mennonite Church Hires World-Famous DJ to Remix Hymn 606

GOSHEN, IN

It's so ubiquitous that it's been called the "Mennonite Anthem," but after more than a century of incessant use, Mennonite Church committee members felt the same old Hymn 606 was growing stale and have hired DJ Nafziger, the most famous electronic dance artist that was available within the confines of their budget, to dramatically overhaul the lyrics and melody of the famous hymn.

"People were just sick of it. 'Praise God from Whom All Blessings Flow' every single Sunday, year after year. Especially the young people. Enough was enough," said DJ Nafziger, adjusting his collar to obscure his neck tattoo from sight. "So I've changed the tune to Taylor Swift's 'Shake It Off' and have added a couple country-rap verses."

A recording of the new hymn, which is set to be released on YouTube a week before the new *Voices Together* hymnal drops, will be known as "Hymn 606 (Nafziger Remix) [featuring 2 Chainz]."

"606 just ain't what she used to be," said Nafziger. "And after my changes, you won't be able to recognize her at all, especially with all that bass thumping in your face. Good luck learning all the new dance moves, Mrs. Kauffman."

Nafziger has also been hired to make changes to several other famous hymns and says he really can't wait for people to hear his new version of "Amazing Grace," which is set to the tune of Michael Jackson's "Smooth Criminal."

FE'SCHLUCKE

(WHEN FOOD OR DRINK GOES DOWN THE WRONG TUBE)

Mennonite Potluck Salads Consist Mostly of Whipped Cream
NEUBERGTHAL, MB

First-time attendees at a recent church potluck were shocked to discover just what passes for salad in Mennonite country. The Thompson family of Winnipeg ventured out of the big city for Neubergthal's annual Darp Days and were baffled by the wide range of "salads," all of which seemed to contain copious amounts of Cool Whip.

"I always thought salad implied some sort of green vegetable, you know, like lettuce or cucumber or something," said Mrs. Thompson, "but these Mennonites have a whole wide world of salad that I wasn't even aware existed."

The outsiders were dazzled by the variety of whipped-cream-based salads at the potluck, which included whipped cream and oranges, whipped cream and pistachios, and whipped cream and cherries.

"That last one also contained a lot of Jell-O," said Thompson. "There wasn't a vegetable to be seen for miles around. It's like these Mennonites consume nothing but gelatin and highly processed dairy."

Potluck organizer Mrs. Carol Brandt was quick to defend the potluck offerings.

"I tried bringing a bean salad once but there were so many leftovers that my Henry was eating nothing but legumes for months," said Brandt. "After that, I learned my lesson. It's whipped cream and marshmallows or bust!"

The Thompsons say they found Mennonite customs a little strange, but after consuming so much sugar on Sunday they've developed a dependence and might be back for next week's potluck.

Meanwhile, Brandt believes Mennonite salads are nothing to be ashamed of.

"Besides," she said, "you should see what passes for salad in Germany."

Buns Discovered in Mennonite Grandma's Freezer Carbon-Dated to 5 Million Years Old

TABER, AB

A bag full of frozen buns discovered at the back of Grandma Wiebe's freezer this past week was taken to a University of Alberta laboratory to undergo rigorous scientific testing, including carbon dating. The results show the buns date back to the Pliocene epoch and are between three to five million years old.

"So far, these are the oldest *zwieback* we have on record," said Dr. Michelle Quiring. "They've been in the back of Mrs. Wiebe's freezer for millions of years. I'm really surprised they hadn't been discovered until now. I guess no one ever looked past the Pizza Pops."

Scientists also discovered a plastic pail of frozen green bean soup dating to the Cretaceous period and a half-eaten tray of *plautz* from the Jurassic era.

"All these items are in remarkable shape considering their age," said Quiring. "Most of the specimens are museum quality and are still pretty darn tasty after a few minutes in the microwave."

To further her research into Mennonite food preservation practices, Quiring is assembling a team of undergraduates to excavate Mrs. Wiebe's root cellar later in the week.

"We're gonna carbon-date her raspberry preserves and pickled beets and whatever else she's got in those jars down there," said Quiring. "I hear she's accumulated quite the collection of slowly rotting treats."

Dr. Quiring has also received permission from the family to carbon-date Grandpa Wiebe while he sleeps.

Conservative Mennonite Church Approves Drinking Bud Light 'Since It's Not Really Beer Anyway'

JANSEN, NE

A strict Mennonite church in the small town of Jansen, Nebraska has broken decades of teetotaller tradition by approving the consumption of Bud Light. At a membership meeting on Saturday, the church board ruled that Bud Light did not qualify as actual beer.

"It ain't no sin to drink water," said Pastor David. "From now on, all our church *faspas* will include cheese, pickles, and a round or two of Bud Light."

The ruling came after months of extensive research from the elder board, who prefer their Bud Light with a squeeze of lemon and a few ice cubes.

"We got together every Monday night for the past few months to pray, study scripture, and drink Bud Light," explained Pastor David. "Not only did I acquire a taste for light, watery beer, but I'm also now a huge Chiefs fan!"

In all those Monday night Bible studies, the men of the elder board never once got drunk.

"Bud Light is officially approved," said Pastor David. "I can assure you from frequent experience that the contents of this bottle contain absolutely no alcohol or any flavour whatsoever!"

The church has also voted to approve cigarettes so long as the smokers stay out of the Ladies' Quilting Room.

Server Left Waiting Awkwardly at Table for Mennonite Couple to Finish Praying

FARGO, ND

Poor Diana, a third-year NDSU student and part-time server at Chili's, was left standing at the table for half an hour holding a Mix & Match trio of steak, shrimp, and chicken fajitas while the Reimers of Winkler finished praying.

"I didn't want to interrupt, but the food was getting cold and my arms were starting to wobble, so I cleared my throat to get their attention ... but the man just kept on going," explained Diana. "'Bless Timmy back home, and bless Grandma, and bless the hands that have prepared it, and bless our server Diana.' I'm a praying woman myself, but it was too much."

After 15 minutes or so, her other tables were starting to wonder where she was and the manager stopped by to inquire what was up.

"This isn't the first time I've seen this," said restaurant manager Amanda. "Whenever the Mennonites come down for a shopping spree this always happens. But we give them their space and let them just keep on praying. Twenty, 30, 40 minutes. Whatever it takes to get that food blessed and ready to eat."

In an interview after the meal, Mr. Reimer confessed he could sense that Diana was at the table, and even got a nudge from Mrs. Reimer to speed things up and stop being rude, but took a quick glance at the fajitas and figured a little extra prayer wouldn't hurt.

Mennonite Man Hospitalized After Eating Too Far Into the Green Part

CUAUHTÉMOC, MEXICO

M r. Kjnels Barkman was rushed to the hospital in Cuauhtémoc this week after he failed to heed the warnings of all those around him and ate well into the green part.

"*Na*, that *oola* Barkman is naver listening. I told him, 'Kjnels, watch yourself,' but he just doesn't listen," said his cousin Jake. "You've gotta leave a bit of red on there yet."

Oola Barkman explained that he really likes the green part and doesn't see why it needs to be thrown to the pigs.

"Doesn't the *Biebel* say 'don't throw pearls to swine'?" said Barkman. "So why toss out the very bast part of the watermelon yet!"

After eating 15 pieces right to the peel, Kjnels Barkman was found reeling on the ground in agony.

"His discomfort was so bad," said cousin Jake, "that not even Pieta Toews's beet-juice-and-chili-pepper miracle cure could bring him back to normal."

Barkman is currently having his stomach pumped at the hospital in Cuauhtémoc, but claims it was all worth it and that he'll do it all over again at the next church picnic.

Local Man Faces Blasphemy Charges After Putting Ketchup on Perogies

WINKLER, MB

Retired bricklayer Barry Plett of Winkler was arraigned on a wide variety of charges including Espionage, Defacing Public Property, and Attempted Murder after photographic evidence revealed he lathered his cottage cheese *vereniki* in a thick layer of ketchup this past Friday. Prosecutors have also applied a little-known and archaic blasphemy law that's been on the books since the late 1800s.

"In all my years, I've never seen such a disgusting defilement of the beloved Mennonite-style perogy," said Constable Dueck. "You can fry them, you can add onions, you can use sour cream or *schmaunt fat,* but under no circumstances will we tolerate the usage of ketchup!"

If convicted of the charges, Plett could face up to 20 years in prison.

"Back in '86, Mr. Koop was arrested for putting spray-can whipped topping on his heart-shaped waffles," explained Dueck. "He's still behind bars."

Local press has already dubbed Plett the "*Vereniki* Violator" after a published photograph of the ketchup-laden *vereniki* on the front page of the local paper caused three elderly women to faint at the coffee shop.

"I'll feel a lot safer when that man is behind bars," said area woman Edna Harms. "I've lost a lot of sleep over those defiled perogies. They should lock him up and throw away the key."

Plett's lawyers are hoping the jury will be lenient and maybe allow him to serve out his time in the community eating potato and cheese perogies or something.

Mennonite Woman Cancels Italy Trip
After Discovering Olive Garden

LINDEN, AB

An area woman has decided to cancel her upcoming "vacation of a lifetime" to Italy after discovering the rustic regional Italian cuisine of Olive Garden. Mrs. Eleanor Wohlgemuth, a retired nurse from Linden, had planned to spend three weeks in Tuscany this fall, but now says "why bother?"

"Ever since I was a little girl, I've dreamed of going to Italy and seeing the great works of Botticelli and Brunelleschi for myself," said Wohlgemuth. "I've watched every video Rick Steves ever made about Italy. I even bought myself a money belt. But now that I know about Olive Garden breadsticks, I think I'll just stay in rural Alberta forever."

After driving into the city to dine at a Calgary Olive Garden location, Wohlgemuth figured she'd had enough authentic Italian food and couldn't imagine that the deep-fried parmesan zucchini bites were any better in Florence.

"Plus, that salad is to die for," exclaimed Wohlgemuth. "It just keeps coming and coming. Who needs to go all the way to Italy when we've got this amazing restaurant right here in the mall parking lot?"

When asked whether she'd regret not seeing Michelangelo's *David* in person, Wohlgemuth just pointed to the mural on the Olive Garden wall and said, "*Na*, I'm good."

Local Mom Super Excited About Her Brand-New Set of 'Mennonite Tupperware'

DALMENY, SK

Area mom Linda Doerksen, 34, was absolutely pumped when Mrs. Martens dropped off a set of Mennonite Tupperware including three freshly rinsed margarine containers, two slightly used cottage cheese containers, and four totally empty sour cream containers.

"Plus, there were a couple yogurt containers complete with lids!" said Doerksen. "I'm so grateful to Mrs. Martens for her generosity. You know a busy mom like me can always use some more Tupperware!"

The versatile set of empty containers will really come in handy during church *faspa* season this fall.

"I've got a backlog of orders to fulfill," said Doerksen. "My marshmallow-and-canned-pineapple salads are in high demand! It's a good thing I've finally got enough Tupperware to store it all."

Normally Martens sells Mennonite Tupperware for two dollars a set, or individual pieces for 50 cents each, but this time she felt like spreading the love.

"Linda's a young mom and I saw her poor selection of sour cream containers. She didn't even have lids for some of them," said Martens. "I figured I'd help out. I had some empty containers anyway. My George cruises through cottage cheese like nobody's business."

Rumour has it that the local MCC store has a vast selection of Mennonite Tupperware for those who are in the market for a fancy new set of their own.

Farmer-Sausage-Scented Air Fresheners a Big Hit in Mennonite Country

WINKLER, MB

A new *foarmaworscht*-scented car air freshener has been flying off the shelves at Winkler gas stations this past week, with Mennonites throughout the region eager to have their truck cabs smelling of smoked meat.

"Right now, it's hard to keep up with the demand," said air freshener manufacturer Dale Redekop, "but we're ramping up production. We don't want to disappoint the thousands of Mennonites who want that new-sausage aroma."

Redekop says the company is offering Pioneer-, Winkler-, and Schanzenfeld-scented air fresheners, but is hoping to expand to include Spenst, Bergmann, and a local Hutterite variety as well.

"Whatever scent you want, we plan to provide it," said Redekop. "We're also working on a wide range of kubasa scents for our Ukrainian customers."

Redekop explains that the process of manufacturing the air fresheners is very simple.

"We take the unscented air fresheners and just leave them lying around in Winkler homes," said Redekop. "After a month in Grandma Wiebe's kitchen, the air freshener is ready for use."

Redekop says he's also been getting a lot of online sales from Abbotsford Mennonites who, if they have trouble accessing good Mennonite farmer sausage in their area, at least want their cars to smell like it.

"Our product is for everyone," said Redekop, "but please, a friendly reminder, these air fresheners are not for ingestion. Smell them, rub them all over your body if you must, but as tempting as it may be, please do not eat them."

New Mennonite EpiPen Injects Emergency Supply of Schmaunt Fat

PLUM COULEE, MB

Mennonites throughout southern Manitoba have been lining up outside local pharmacies to get their hands on a newly redesigned EpiPen that injects an emergency supply of *schmaunt fat* straight into the user's bloodstream.

"We're confident this new *schmaunt fat* EpiPen will save thousands of lives," said inventor and physician Dr. Larry Esau. "There are times when Mennonites are low on *schmaunt fat*, or they've come into contact with too many vegetables, and they need a direct injection to keep their *schmaunt fat* levels steady."

Concerned parent Mary Hamm of Plum Coulee was first in line to purchase the new medical device.

"I'm usually pretty good at monitoring my own *schmaunt fat* intake to make sure I'm getting enough," said Hamm, "but sometimes I worry about my son and whether he's taking in sufficient amounts of the white cream gravy. I just hope I can convince him to carry his EpiPen with him all the time."

New users of the EpiPen are being asked to practice injecting *schmaunt fat* on a partner, so that in an emergency they will remain calm and be able to provide a life-saving dose of the delicious sludge.

"You flip off the cap and slam the needle into the patient's thigh," said Dr. Esau. "By the time you count to 10, the *schmaunt fat* is already working."

At press time, it is not known whether Blue Cross insurance will cover the new apparatus.

McDonald's to Offer All-Day Faspa
WINNIPEG, MB

Thanks to mounting pressure from many of their loyal Mennonite customers, the world's largest fast-food chain is experimenting with all-day *faspa* in a half-dozen stores across Western Canada.

"We've been listening to customers in Steinbach, Winkler, and North Kildonan. They've been demanding all-day *faspa* for years," said McDonald's spokesperson Alissa Larson. "We're rolling it out in six stores for now. If it's successful, we'll expand all-day *faspa* nationwide."

At the six restaurants, customers will now be able to order yellow mustard and *fleesch perishky* the moment the store opens, rather than only between the hours of 3:00 and 5:00 on a Sunday afternoon.

"I'm super excited to be able to get a good McDonald's *faspa* whenever I want it," said Rod Kroeker of North Kildonan. "Sometimes I'm there at 8:00 a.m. and all I want is a good slice of rolled up ham or a handful of Bothwell cheese curds, but no, for whatever reason I'd have to wait until the afternoon. I'm sure glad they've changed their policy."

So far, all-day *faspa* has also been popular with the late-night bar-hopping crowd.

"Once the bars close up at 2:00 a.m., all the Mennonite drinkers stop by for a nice warm *schnetje*," said Larson. "We're really glad to finally be able to offer *faspa* wherever and whenever the people want it."

A Closet-Drinker's Guide to *The Mennonite Treasury Cookbook*

The Mennonite Treasury of Recipes offers a veritable bounty of classic Mennonite recipes. However, until now, Mennonites were left completely on their own when determining what beverage to closet-drink with their chosen dish. Thanks to extensive testing and consultation with expert Mennonite sommeliers, Mennonites can now accurately pair a wine, beer, or other beverage with their favourite dish.

- Green bean soup (page 17)

  The delicate flavours of bean and farmer sausage in this classic *jreen schaubel supp* recipe by Mrs. Reimer of Steinbach pairs well with an elegant German Riesling such as the Wittmann Aulerde or Gustav Adolf Schmitt Clean Slate from Mosel. Please, for the sake of all that is good in the world, don't forget to "take off scum while cooking meat," as Mrs. Reimer suggests.

- Cottage cheese cakes (page 22)

  The fried *glums koki* is the dirtier, greasier cousin of the boiled *vereniki*, and as such, pairs well with a flavourful craft beer such as Half Pints Little Scrapper IPA or a Rendezvous Stephen Street Sour. Mrs. Peters may not approve of hops, but your taste buds will when they try this intriguing flavour combination.

- Ruehrei (page 16)

  Whether you eat them with syrup or, as my grandfather did, with vinegar, this Mennonite scrambled egg dish is versatile and satisfying, thus suited for a wide variety of pairing options. I like my *ruehrei* with a pisco sour or a nice gin and tonic or five.

- Foarmaworscht

  There is no recipe for farmer sausage in the cookbook because everyone already knows how to cook it, and some people even eat it raw. The smoked Mennonite delicacy pairs well with an Islay Scotch, such as Lagavulin 16, which has a robust peaty nose that matches perfectly with a Pioneer or Schanzenfeld *foarmaworscht*.

- Rhubarb plautz (page 9)

  Rhubarb is a complex fruit (or weed or whatever it is), with an intensely tart taste. *The Daily Bonnet* recommends fighting sour with sour and so a Flemish red ale such as Duchesse de Bourgogne or a Cantillon lambic will provide a suitably puckering experience.

- Plümemoos (page 21)

  Choking down grandma's *plümemoos* requires a great deal of lubrication. In this case, we recommend something cheap and fast like a two-litre plastic bottle of malt liquor, or perhaps your uncle's moonshine or dandelion wine. Whatever you decide, you're going to need something to get that *plümemoos* down your gullet.

- Dill pickles (page 199)

  The Mennonite Treasury offers almost two dozen different pickle recipes. Although some strange Mennonites can tolerate the sweetness of a bread-and-butter pickle, the more common choice is a crisp, sour dill pickle such as the one described by Eva Neufeld of Niverville on page 199. The pickle works surprisingly well with the tingly palate of a Champagne or, since we're all Mennonites here, a cheaper sparkling wine from another region where they make the exact same thing at half the price.

- Schmaunt fat (page 14)

  For a cookbook full of Mennonite recipes, it's actually surprising there is only one recipe for white cream gravy. *The Daily Bonnet* recommends remaining completely sober when consuming *schmaunt fat*, and in extreme cases of thirst, the *schmaunt fat* may be poured into one of those big German beer steins and drunk straight.

- Klopps (page 97)

  There are very few Mennonite dishes that can hold up to a robust red wine, but *klopps* (or meatballs) made with chunks of onion and breadcrumbs is one of them. A few dozen *klopps* goes well with a bottle of Gouguenheim Reserva Malbec, just don't tell anyone you drank the whole bottle or ate all the *klopps*.

As always, please closet-drink responsibly.

Mennonite Woman's 'Abstinence in a Pan' Declared Worst Dessert at Church Bake Sale

NEWTON, KS

The Newton Mennonite Church Bake Sale generated lower than expected revenue this week, due in part to the extreme unpopularity of Mrs. Deirdre Jansen's Abstinence in a Pan dessert. The dessert contained layers of corn flakes, prunes, and extra-salty soda crackers.

"For years people brought that 'other dessert,' which I won't mention. It was leading people astray, giving them impure thoughts," explained Jansen. "I figured it was time to promote a more family-friendly message. What better way to do that than with a bland, disgusting dessert that no one finds the least bit titillating?"

Jansen had been working on the recipe for Abstinence in a Pan for quite some time and was shocked by the low sales.

"It just proves how far we've fallen from the true message of the Gospel," said Jansen. "It's a sad state of affairs when even church folks want to buy nothing but tasty and sexually suggestive desserts."

Jansen made more than 30 trays of Abstinence in a Pan, which she baked every evening for the past month.

"Every time Howard was getting a little too frisky, I just told him I was baking," said Jansen. "I may not have sold a lot of that dessert at the church bake sale, but it sure lived up to its name around our household."

Prior to her ingenious invention of Abstinence in a Pan, Jansen had always just told Howard she was "washing her hair" or "reading the Bible." In response to his wife's new dessert, Howard reportedly bought up all the Sex in a Pan he could get at this year's bake sale.

Knackzoat Found in Last Summer's Jean Shorts
'Still Perfectly Edible' Says Local Man
ALTONA, MB

Local man Ernie Toews, 75, considered himself the "luck-iest man in Altona" this past Saturday after he slid into a pair of old cut-off jean shorts that he hadn't worn since last summer, only to find that the pockets were filled to the brim with "perfectly edible" sunflower seeds.

"I thought I had won the lottery," said Toews, who enjoyed the *zoat* while watching a local slo-pitch game. "Two whole pockets' worth of un*knacked knackzoat* yet! *Oba jo!*"

Toews witnessed the Altona Dirty Tractors defeat the Gretna Re-baptizers 15-11 while munching away on his delicious, only slightly stale, sunflower seeds.

"They still spit perfectly fine," said Toews, showing off his *zoat*-projecting skills. "Look at that. I nearly hit the third baseman."

Toews plans to go home immediately after the game and check all his other pants pockets to see what treasures he might find.

"You never know what Martha left in there yet," said Toews. "Some loose change? A crumpled Kleenex? If I'm lucky maybe even a Ravel bar and a Papsi to boot!"

The supply of sunflower seeds carried Toews to the end of the fifth inning when he had to purchase a new bag, which he promptly emptied into his pockets.

"They always taste better coming straight from the pocket," said Toews, "and you know, a little lint never hurt anybody."

City of Winkler to Abandon the Metric System in Favour of Ice-Cream-Pail Method

WINKLER, MB

Beginning this fall, residents of Winkler will be forced to measure everything in the traditional Mennonite manner—using the ice cream pail. In a 5-2 vote, Winkler's city council decided to ban the use of the metric system and replace it with well-rinsed plastic pails.

"Ever since the elder Trudeau introduced it in the 1970s, people have been confused about the metric system. I think the best solution is to go back to the method of measurement that every Mennonite knows best, and that is the ice cream pail," explained city councillor Elbert Sawatzky. "It really is the most efficient measurement system known to humankind."

Mennonites have traditionally used ice cream pails to quantify everything from blueberries picked in the Whiteshell to the liquid volume of coleslaw and potato salad.

"We've standardized the measurement with Taunte Annie's ammonia cookies, which were always pretty consistent in size and weight. She could fit 52 cookies in one ice cream pail, so from now on we'll be measuring everything on a 52-point scale," explained Sawatzky. "The hardware store is really looking forward to the change."

Local schools are already teaching their children how to figure out their height and weight in ice cream pails and the municipality is considering measuring distances with this method. According to the new system, Winkler is precisely 39,367 ice cream pails from Morden.

"Farmers are already talking about how many hectare-pails of flax they've planted," noted Sawatzky. "This ice-cream-pail method is just going to make life a lot easier on everybody."

Grandkids Still Reluctant to Go Anywhere Near Oma's Plümemoos

REINLAND, MB

The unveiling of Oma's famous Easter *plümemoos* this Sunday sent little Erika and Carter Brandt running for the hills and screaming at the top of their lungs. Erika, 4, and Carter, 6, are not used to the sight, smell, or texture of Oma's cold plum soup.

"Ach, those children yet! All they want are Oreo cookies," exclaimed Oma Brandt. "I tried to sit them down on my lap and spoon the clumpy reddish-brown liquid into them, but they were having none of it."

The fact that Oma's *plümemoos* closely resembles the sludge that Mom pulls from the bathroom sink every other week was a determining factor in Erika and Carter's reluctance to try it.

"I know it doesn't look like much, but once they try it, I'm sure they'll be hooked," said Oma. "If only I could trick them into tasting it somehow."

Oma then sprayed an entire can of Cool Whip onto the *plümemoos* and handed each child a bowl.

"At first they were very excited, but as soon as they got past the imitation whipped topping, the crying started up again," said Oma. "I'm really at my wits' end with these two."

Oma Brandt is especially concerned because the local Mennonite church will not allow them membership unless they learn to stomach *plümemoos*.

"They've still got a few years left to acquire a taste," said Oma, "but by the time they've learned their catechism they've got to be able to down a bowl of this stuff. Otherwise they'll never get baptized and married!"

At press time, Oma Brandt was having equal difficulty convincing the kids to try her *somma borscht*.

Mennonites Compete to See Who Can Cook the Blandest, Least Spicy Chili

LEAMINGTON, ON

Mennonites across southern Ontario have gathered in Leamington this week for the annual MB-GC Chili Cook-Off. Returning to the competition is last year's champion Mrs. Clara Snyder of Elmira, whose extra-bland, zero-pepper chili delighted the judges.

"She's a miracle worker with a bottle of ketchup and a can of tomatoes," said head judge Mr. Leonard Fehr. "I mean, when you can make a chili as unspicy as Mrs. Snyder's, it's really difficult for the others to compete. How can you make it any blander?"

Mennonites have a notoriously low tolerance for spicy food, and the judges are always looking for a nice simple chili that consists entirely of unseasoned ground beef and a few kidney beans.

"Spicy food unnecessarily riles up the senses and gets people thinking unwholesome thoughts," said Fehr. "It's the same reason we ply our children with dry puffed wheat every morning."

Mrs. Snyder is facing fierce competition this year from the Wiens family of Aylmer who have been working on their recipe all year.

"I think we've got it down to the level where even Oma can tolerate it ... although she did request to add a little sour cream to the last batch," said Wiens. "However, after a few tweaks, we guarantee no one will be breaking into a sweat with our Wienses' Secret Extra-Mild Chili!"

The winner will be declared on Sunday after a sleep-inducing sermon by Pastor Gerald.

Mennonite Man Leaves Record $0.10 Tip at Local Diner
STEINBACH, MB

A rea waitresses were shocked to hear of the generous 10-cent tip that fellow restaurant server Mary Penner received during her evening shift on Saturday.

"In all my years of waitressing, I've never received such a huge tip," said Penner. "I just wish I could reach out to the man who left it and send him my gratitude and appreciation."

Penner plans to put the 10-cent tip in her child's college fund.

"Normally people are just getting rid of their pennies," said Penner, "but when the elderly gentleman rummaged around in his pocket and pulled out a shiny new dime, I was left speechless."

The previous Steinbach tip record of one nickel and two pennies was set by Mr. Abram R. Funk at The Jolly Miller in 1991. The Steinbach Historical Society placed a plaque on the site to commemorate the event. Perhaps not coincidentally, the record was broken precisely 25 years to the day after Funk's historic donation.

"I really hope I can track down the man who left me this dime," Penner said. "I think he deserves a plaque too. These two men are the pioneers of generosity who make this job worthwhile."

Mennonite Woman Tries to Pass Off Blueberry Pie as Saskatoon Pie

NEUANLAGE, SK

Mrs. Tina Krahn is in hot water this week after bringing what was clearly a blueberry pie to the Neuanlage soup and pie fundraiser and labelling it "saskatoon-berry pie."

"Who does she think she's kidding? These are store-bought blueberries! Anyone can see that," said rival pie-maker Mrs. Marilyn Thiessen. "Who does she think we are? City people who can't tell the difference? Maybe she thinks we're Americans or something."

At first, a few inattentive pie lovers inadvertently took a piece, but it didn't take long for the deceptive blueberry pie to be discovered ... and discarded.

"Ugh, it doesn't taste the same at all. Saskatoons are much sweeter and tastier!" said Mrs. Thiessen. "Only an amateur would be fooled by these dreadful blueberries! *Oba,* that Mrs. Krahn. That woman knew full well what she was doing when she signed up for this fundraiser. I bet she thought some extra sugar would save it. Well, Tina, it certainly does not!"

Mrs. Krahn has been charged with Public Mischief, Fraud, and Impersonating a Saskatoon. If convicted, she will be forced to spend all her weekends this summer sweating it out in the bush gathering wild saskatoon berries with Mrs. Thiessen.

Mourners Devastated After Mennonite Funeral Runs Short on Raisin Buns

SOUTH BLUMENORT, MB

Thousands of Mennonites were expecting to gorge on raisin buns at the Sawatzky funeral this past week but were left in tears when the organizers ran out of their supply after just one serving.

"It was utterly devastating. The mood sure dampened after that," said Mrs. Krause. "It had been a festive atmosphere, but that all changed pretty quick when we ran out of raisin buns!"

When the second round of buns came by and funeral-goers started to realize they were just regular white buns, the Sawatzky funeral really took a turn.

"I don't want to be a downer, but we're out of raisin buns," announced funeral volunteer Mrs. Klassen. "I'm really sorry. I know how much these raisin buns meant to you. They were close to me too. It's sad to see them go."

Soon a slide show featuring photographs of various raisin buns over the years, accompanied by Christian praise music, was being projected on the walls of the church gymnasium.

"It's good to mourn like this," said Mrs. Krause, who stood at the mic for nearly an hour during the *freiwilliges,* sharing many of her favourite raisin bun memories. "The loss of the raisin buns is going to be hard on all of us, but I am confident these raisin buns will live on forever in our hearts."

Noticing the increasingly agitated and distraught crowd, Pastor Frank addressed the audience with a few words of consolation.

"Friends, we do not grieve as those without hope," he said. "Someday there will be another funeral and on that glorious day we can hope and pray that the organizers will be better prepared with more raisin buns. Amen."

In lieu of flowers, donations can be made to the South Blumenort Raisin Bun Procurement Fund.

Mennonite Woman Discovers $1,000,000 in
Deceased Oma's Margarine Containers

WALDHEIM, SK

Area woman Barb Rempel was helping to clean up her recently deceased grandmother's house this week when she made a discovery that will change the course of her life forever. On the upper floor of Oma Rempel's Waldheim house, Barb found a closet full of margarine containers.

"At first I thought nothing of it," said Barb, "but then I flipped open one Becel lid and discovered it was full of dimes and nickels … and there were a lot more margarine containers where that one came from."

By the time all the margarine containers full of coins were added up, the money totalled more than $993,000, which Barb says she plans to share with all her cousins.

"Each of us should get about $300, which is a pretty nice sum," said Barb. "All I can say is thanks a lot, Oma!"

It is not known how long it took the elder Mrs. Rempel to accumulate this volume of pocket change, but officials are saying this method of banking is not uncommon among Mennonites.

"We're asking all the Mennonite families out there to keep on the look-out for margarine containers," said financial advisor Petey B. Epp. "You never know what you might find besides just, you know, margarine."

Just days after the discovery, Barb Rempel had already spent her cut of the money on the biggest MCC shopping spree northern Saskatchewan has ever seen.

Curry Dish Confuses Attendees at Old Colony Potluck
LEAMINGTON, ON

It was just a regular Sunday after-church potluck for members of Leamington Old Colony Mennonite Church. That is, until Lydia Neufeld showed up with butter chicken.

"I couldn't figure out what on earth it was supposed to be," said baffled diner Henry Dyck. "This looks nothing like *vereniki* to me."

The presence of the curry dish caused quite the stir as confused Mennonite seniors attending the luncheon tried to make sense of the mysterious cuisine.

"Should I put it at the front of the line, or the back, and how close to the potato salad should it go?" wondered event organizer Rebecca Block. "In the end, I decided to put it next to the sugar cubes and hope for the best."

Neufeld, who brought the dish, says she was told to bring "good old-fashioned Mennonite cooking," but was confused by what that meant.

"I heard from a missionary last Sunday that there are more Mennonites these days in India than there are in North America," she said. "It was an honest mistake. I'm truly sorry."

Attendees filled their paper plates with processed ham slices, dill pickles, and marble cheese, and somehow, they all found that their plates were "much too full" by the time they reached the butter chicken, though a few particularly polite Mennonites managed to squeeze a tiny dollop on the edge of their plates.

Inspired by Neufeld's efforts in Leamington, editors of *The Mennonite Treasury of Recipes* are considering adding chicken tikka masala, onion pakora, and saag paneer to their next edition of the cookbook under the category "Food We Can't Make Heads or Tails of but Seems to Taste Pretty Good Anyway."

Chef Gordon Ramsay Has Absolutely No Criticism for Mennonite Girls

ABBOTSFORD, BC

Surly British chef and TV host Gordon Ramsay was briefly tongued-tied on Friday after being stunned by the kitchen chops of Mennonite cookbook author Lovella Schellenberg and her team when they appeared on Ramsay's television show.

The host of *Hell's Kitchen* and *MasterChef* usually rips chefs apart, leaving them crying into their soup by the end of each episode, but Ramsay was so impressed with the Mennonite Girls that he offered no criticism for the first time in his career.

"What can I say?" said Ramsay. "The culinary abilities of these Mennonite women are unparalleled in the history of network television cooking shows."

The Mennonite Girls impressed the famed chef with Ellen's hamburger soup recipe and Anneliese's meatballs with mushroom sauce before leaving him speechless with Charlotte's Toblerone cheesecake.

"The Mennonite Girls sure cook with soul," said Ramsay. "There's not a single thing I would change about any of these dishes."

Ramsay says he plans to make the *Mennonite Girls Can Cook* cookbook mandatory reading for chefs in all his restaurants and is considering modifying the format of *Hell's Kitchen* to allow for more Mennonite content, although he's already been told the show's title will need to change if he hopes to attract many Mennonite guests.

Manitoba Couple Forgets to Bring the 'Good Farmer Sausage' on Trip to Alberta

TABER, AB

The Doerksens of Kleefeld disappointed a whole community of Alberta Mennonites this week after completely forgetting to bring the "good farmer sausage" with them on a recent trip.

"We were in such a rush, it just slipped my mind," said Mrs. Doerksen. "I feel really bad. I know how devastating it can be to go months with just whatever farmer sausage they can get out there in Alberta."

The Alberta relatives were so upset that they made the Doerksens sleep on the old hide-a-bed from the '70s.

"That'll teach them to forget my *foarmaworscht*!" said cousin Rudy. "Let's see how their backs feel after a night on that old thing!"

Although the Alberta Mennonites have been able to replicate *schmaunt fat* without much difficulty, for some reason farmer sausage has always been a challenge.

"It just ain't the same," said Rudy. "The guy around here puts too much garlic in it or something."

Cousin Rudy says he's strongly considering moving to Manitoba and will gladly put up with the frigid weather so long as he can get the good stuff whenever he wants.

Impossible to Tell if Bearded Friend Is Mennonite or Just Really Into Craft Beer

GOSHEN, IN

When a bearded young man named David moved to Goshen from the country a few months ago, his physical appearance had friendly locals unsure if they should invite him to a Bible study or offer him a hazy IPA.

"I couldn't figure it out at first," said area resident Peter Showalter. "With a beard like that, the guy's either some kind of Mennonite or just really into microbrews. No matter what I said I risked offending him, so instead I just asked whether he'd like to go for coffee or whatever ..."

A few weeks later, the new friends were walking by Goshen Brewing Company where David was stopped by a staff member and told he was late for work.

"Straightaway they had him adding hops to the boil kettle and all that," said Showalter. "I'm surprised he even knew what they were asking him to do. As far as I knew, all he spoke was Pennsylvania Dutch."

After proving himself at the brewery for a few weeks, David got himself a nice white V-neck T-shirt and a couple tattoos.

"I'm still confused about David. He's a hard, conscientious worker with a thick beard," said Showalter, "but he sure knows a heck of a lot about Vienna malt."

To add to the confusion, David was also spotted the very next Sunday with his fixed-gear bicycle in the parking lot of East Goshen Mennonite Church.

City's Top Chef Mortified to Discover His Charcuterie Board Is Just Glorified Faspa

VANCOUVER, BC

The chef at one of Vancouver's top restaurants has been feeding the city's elite for years with his delectable selection of charcuterie. Unfortunately, Chef Pierre Poirier's ego took a big hit this weekend after a trip to neighbouring Abbotsford.

"I got invited to something called *faspa*," said Poirier, "which I learned was a meal consisting of deli meats and dill pickles held in a stuffy church basement. And it dawned on me, as I buttered my raisin bun, that the charcuterie plate I've been charging $39.99 for at my restaurant was really just fancy *faspa*."

The epiphany had Chef Poirier making major changes to his Vancouver restaurant.

"From now on, no more Iberico ham and pheasant terrine," said Poirier. "Instead, we're going to offer rolled-up slices of mystery meat and a delectable array of mild cheddar. We're still charging 40 bucks but, you know …"

Chef Poirier assures customers that only the finest cuts of bologna will make it onto his Mennonite charcuterie board, which will be served on Styrofoam plates to keep things "authentic."

"Everyone is invited to overpay for our new *faspa* board," said Poirier. "For an additional charge of just $52, we will be happy to pair your *faspa* with our sommelier's finest selection of tap water or instant coffee."

The restaurant will charge a $20 corkage fee if you want to bring your own church-basement red juice.

Steinbach Residents to Vote on Whether to Acknowledge Each Other in the Liquor Store

STEINBACH, MB

For decades, the Mennonite town of Steinbach, Manitoba was officially dry. No liquor could be bought or sold anywhere in the region. However, a number of referendums have taken place over the years that have seen Steinbach liberalize its liquor laws, and today the town boasts a handful of bars and one liquor store. This fall, the residents of Steinbach will vote on whether they will acknowledge each other in these establishments or simply avoid eye contact and pretend not to notice each other like they currently do.

"The only time I ever saw a Steinbacher drink was in Playa del Carmen last winter," said local closet-drinker Otto P. Martens. "No one I know admits to buying beer at the local liquor store. I'm not sure how that place stays open. I've never been in there, myself ... or at least there's no proof I have."

The ballot will be kept simple; residents will check *jo* or *nä*. If passed, residents must smile and shake hands when they see someone they know, just like they do in the grocery store.

"It will be quite the change to the liquor-shopping experience," said Martens, who claims he's voting *nä* in September's poll. "Not that I know anything about that. I did drive past the liquor store once, but I was concerned my car might get spotted in the lot, so I made a beeline for the Superstore and thankfully I wasn't reported to the elders."

Also on the ballot is whether or not shoppers should stand just outside the exit and talk for a long time before saying "*na jo dan*" a few times and then leaving with their purchases.

Mennonite Woman Uses the Same Tea Bag for a Record 10 Years

BLUMENORT, MB

Area woman Ms. Dolores B. Pankratz, 87, has just tied the Blumenort record for continual use of a single tea bag. Reporters will be present at her afternoon women's Bible study tomorrow where she will officially pass Mrs. Irene Plett's record of 10 years, three months, and eight days.

"I'm really excited to break Mrs. Plett's record," said Ms. Pankratz. "This Earl Grey tea bag has been with me through thick and thin, in sickness and in health. It's been my lone companion on long, cold winter nights."

Pankratz claims she can still squeeze some flavour out of the bag, which she nicknamed Kenny, and doesn't see why everyone else around here is so eager to throw out their bags after just three or four uses.

"*Na oba lied ekj saj*! I just can't believe how wasteful everyone is," said Ms. Pankratz. "Little Kenny here has provided me with more than 4,000 cups of tea and he's not done yet!"

Even though friends and relatives have urged Pankratz to give it up and donate the tea bag to missionaries, Pankratz says she has no plans to retire Kenny anytime soon.

"Mrs. Plett's record is going to be left in the dust by the time I'm finished with my precious Kenny," said Pankratz. "You might even have to bury me with him."

Ms. Pankratz has already bought a twin plot at the local cemetery.

'I Could Make It Myself Better and Cheaper': Mennonite Woman Refuses to Buy Anything at Church Bake Sale
GRUNTHAL, MB

While examining the offerings at the Grunthal Church fundraising bake sale this week, Mrs. Greta Kehler refused to buy a single item, claiming that everything she saw she could easily make at home "much better and much, much cheaper yet!"

"Three dollars for a six-pack of molasses cookies? *Oba nä!*" exclaimed Mrs. Kehler. "Or how about this banana loaf over here? Mine is far moister, and cheaper too!"

Mrs. Kehler continued on like this until her daughter Alice reminded her that this whole thing was a fundraiser to buy new, less-slivery church pews.

"Of course you can make it cheaper, Mom," explained Alice. "They're trying to generate some money here!"

Mrs. Kehler was offended at the suggestion.

"Not on my watch, they're not!" she said. "Ach, these butter tarts over here! How many raisins did Mrs. Unger even put in these things? Looks like she's been skimping. And oh, look at that, Mrs. Bartsch is trying to sell her doilies. First of all, doesn't she know this is a bake sale? And secondly, everyone knows Mrs. Bartsch's doilies are inferior to mine! Her stitching is all wrong. All wrong!"

Eventually, Mrs. Kehler had to be escorted out of the building, as she was starting to deter other customers.

"It's all overpriced crap!" yelled Mrs. Kehler at everyone entering the church. "Don't be fooled! If you want good *schnetje*, you've got to come to the Kehler residence!"

Bake sale co-ordinator Mrs. Froese says she had begged Mrs. Kehler to contribute her own baked goods to the sale, but Mrs. Kehler had refused, saying that she didn't have the time to bake these days and would much rather complain.

Local Man Peter Penner Picks a Peck of Pickled Peppers
PANSY, MB

Pastor Peter Penner of Pansy has been pruning his precious peppers and is now prepared to pick a peck of them.

"It's not often you pick a peck of peppers, and these particular peppers are pre-pickled," said Penner. "Peculiar."

Peter Penner noted that his pal Pete Peters had also pondered picking peppers, but perhaps Pete Peters preferred to pick pickled peppers with Pat Plett instead.

"Previously, I've picked many a pepper with Penner," proclaimed Peters. "In Paraguay, we'd pickle peppers in parsley and Papsi, but I promised peaceful Pat Plett that I'd pack them in Port like the pagans prefer."

So, precisely how many pickled peppers did passionate Peter Penner pick?

"I piled a pail of them, practically. They're *prachtvoll*," piped Peter Penner, practicing Plautdietsch. "It's a pair of pecks to a pail, so plenty."

A Calorie Guide to Mennonite Cooking

In the days before we became lazy and assimilated, Mennonites wouldn't concern themselves with such things as counting calories. We worked hard all day on the farm, where we could easily sweat out even the very fattiest of meals, but times have changed. *Oba*, some of us even work in offices yet. So before you dive into that plate of *vereniki* or cracklings, be sure to check our handy calorie-counting guide to common Mennonite dishes. Most of these are Russian Mennonite cuisine, but we included a few dishes from our Swiss Mennonite friends because we want to keep them as healthy and svelte as us Russian Mennos.

(By way of comparison, a Big Mac Meal with medium fries and a medium cola is 1080 calories.)

- A stalk of raw rhubarb

  I know some heathens like to add sugar to their rhubarb, but that ruins the taste and adds unnecessary calories. This is truly a Menno diet food if you enjoy it the way the Lord intended it, without sugar. TOTAL: 11 calories.

- Borscht

  I suppose there are a few Mennos out there who prefer beet *borscht*, but they're usually excommunicated pretty quickly. Cabbage *borscht* (the only real *borscht*) is a bit higher in calories than beet *borscht*, but we can handle it. Beet *borscht* has just 78 calories per cup. Real Mennos are unafraid to go cabbage. TOTAL: 133 calories (including sour cream).

- Friendship bread

  It's not that we aren't friendly (it's even on our license plates here in Manitoba), but most Russian Mennonites have never even heard of this dish. Don't you think if the Swiss Mennos and Amish truly wanted our friendship they'd be a little more generous with their bread recipes? Friendship bread is not too friendly on the waistline, however. TOTAL: 195 calories.

- Faspa

  This is by far the lightest meal a Mennonite typically ever eats: five or six pickles, a handful of cheese curds, a few slices of rolled-up ham, and a *zwieback* with butter. Well, the pickles are high in sodium but have very few calories, only about 7 each. You might have another 100 calories in cheese curds. The ham slices will be about 34 calories each. One *zwieback* might be about 90 calories, plus another 36 for the pat of butter. You've gotta count your calories at those Mennonite funerals. TOTAL: 370 calories.

- Cracklings on toast

  No wonder Oma made Opa have puffed wheat for breakfast once in a while. You just can't have *jreewe* every day. A typical calorie count for 50 grams of cracklings is 272, plus another 210 for the toast with butter. The total is almost twice as much as a Big Mac. TOTAL: 482 calories.

- Schnetje with jam

  Jauma lied, I'm getting hungry now! Two of these Menno biscuits will be around 425 calories, plus 80 calories for the jam. If you have farmer-sausage-stuffed *schnetje* with beef gravy, you're looking at closer to 700. TOTAL: 505-710 calories.

- Mennonite dessert

  Pfeffernüsse/päpanät are 53 calories each. A piece of shoofly pie, beloved by our Pennsylvania Dutch friends, is a whopping 404 calories. One piece of fruit *plautz* is 150 calories. Assuming it's an after-church function and you try one of each to be polite, you're looking at quite the number. TOTAL: 607 calories.

- Knackzoat

  This one was a little surprising. Just one cup of sunflower seeds (with the shell) is 285 calories. Based on the mountainous heap of shells beneath Taunte Lina's lawn chair, I'm guessing she consumes a lot more than that. TOTAL: 855 calories.

- Roll kuchen with Rogers Golden Syrup and watermelon

  One piece of *roll kuchen* is 108 calories. Two tablespoons of Rogers Golden is 138 calories. Each wedge of watermelon is 87 calories. So, at a modest rate of three pieces of *roll kuchen*, six tablespoons of syrup, and two watermelon wedges, you're going to rack up quite the calorie count. TOTAL: 912 calories.

- Foarmaworscht and vereniki with schmaunt fat

  Well, let's see, normally you're gonna eat at least half a pound of farmer sausage, so that's 600 calories right there. A typical *vereniki* is somewhere between 80 and 100 calories, so that's another 480-600 calories if you stop yourself at six and don't fry them. The *schmaunt fat* adds another 300 calories if you use as much as my Onkel Jakob usually does. TOTAL: 1380-1500 calories.

The moral of the story: stick to raw rhubarb and you'll be just fine.

Mennonite Woman Consumes 4L of Ice Cream Just for the Pail

SOMMERFELD, MB

Mrs. Helen Braun of Sommerfeld was so desperate for a fresh used ice cream pail this week that she downed four litres of Foremost chocolate ice cream in one epic evening.

"I was looking at my collection of storage containers and I said to myself, 'Helen, you're running low,'" explained Braun. "I had no choice but to run over to the local Co-op and fetch myself a pail and then eat the entire thing in one sitting."

Wanting to keep her stock of "Mennonite Tupperware" at sufficient numbers for this fall's potluck season, Mrs. Braun intends to eat a four-litre container of ice cream every couple days for the duration of the summer.

"My Kjnels can help, but only if he's willing to do the dishes," said Mrs. Braun. "Otherwise it's just me, five hours of *Tiger King,* and a bucket of Neapolitan!"

Braun insists that it's not about the ice cream per se, but about the container left afterwards.

"The pail is half the value at least," she said. "Most of the time I'm rinsing it out and filling it with macaroni salad before I even get all the way to the bottom."

Meanwhile, Kjnels Braun plans to *knack* tonnes and tonnes of *zoat* this summer, just so he has enough shells to patch the holes in his driveway.

Lutheran Man Joins Mennonite Church After Discovering Roll Kuchen

FRIEDENSFELD, MB

Mr. Günter Freund of Friedensfeld has been a life-long attendee at the local Lutheran church. However, after discovering *roll kuchen* this week, he decided to abandon the faith of his childhood and join the Mennonites.

"*Diewel*, that *roll kuchen* is delicious!" said Freund. "See, look at that, those Mennonites have even got me speaking Plautdietsch!"

Freund had simply wanted to transfer his church membership, but the Mennonite church insisted he had to be rebaptized.

"I'll do whatever it takes. Douse me in Golden Syrup for all I care," said Freund. "As long as I'm guaranteed a lifetime of *roll kuchen*, I'll do anything those adult-baptizing Mennonites ask of me."

Pastor Jake was not surprised by Freund's eagerness to convert.

"I'll let you in on a little secret," said Jake. "*Roll kuchen* has been our most effective evangelistic tool for decades. It's even worked on a few Anglicans from the city."

The church has recently released a new illustrated gospel tract that features a picture of a wide gulf between God and humanity.

"And, in between," said Pastor Jake, "is a bridge made of *roll kuchen*. I think it's the most theologically sound gospel tract we've ever produced."

New Study: Farmer Sausage Contains Only 'Trace Amounts' of Actual Farmers

TOFIELD, AB

A new farmer sausage study from the University of Tubular Meat in Tofield, Alberta suggests that the vast majority of farmer sausage is actually completely farmerless.

"I'm not sure what they're putting in there, but it ain't farmers," said Dr. Violet Janz. "We tested pork sausage, deer sausage, turkey bacon, and all of those lived up to their names, except for farmer sausage."

While the farmer sausage mostly tested negative for farmer, the study showed that a few pieces of *foarmaworscht* did, in fact, contain farmers.

"But only trace amounts," said Dr. Janz. "That could easily just be from when Mr. Kornelsen forgot to wash his hands. It's negligible."

Dr. Janz held a press conference on the steps of the Tofield church this afternoon urging folks to stop calling it farmer sausage and instead call it "ground pork in long intestinal casings," which she says is much more accurate and also "much more delicious-sounding."

Mennonite Woman Nearly Fe'schluckes Herself

NEUHORST, SK

A particularly side-splitting joke at the Harder-Peters wedding reception this weekend almost meant the demise of Mrs. Gloria Epp, 71, of Neuhorst, who came awfully close to *fe'schluck*ing herself. Witnesses say Mrs. Epp had reached for a glass of water just as the joke about Peter and Anna's wedding night reached the punchline.

"*Oba*, looks like Mrs. Epp nearly *fe'schluck*ed herself," said quick-thinking Sheila Heinrichs, reaching around her *fe'schluck*ing friend and applying a good thrust. "There was water everywhere. On her blouse, in my face, and most certainly down the wrong tube."

Thanks to Mrs. Heinrichs's adept abdominal thrusting, Mrs. Epp was saved from her near *fe'schluck*ing.

"*Jauma*! I've got to be a little more careful at these wedding receptions," said Mrs. Epp. "People really should think long and hard before taking a sip of water when that hysterical Melvin Penner is emceeing. I wouldn't want anyone else to *fe'schlucke* themselves like I did."

This was not Mrs. Epp's first encounter with water going down the wrong tube, having nearly *fe'schluck*ed herself at Timothy Plett's baptism in 1987, Doris Petkau's funeral back in 1998, and Gerry and Helen Loeppky's 50th wedding anniversary in 2002.

"I should have been better prepared," said Mrs. Epp. "If I ever *fe'schlucke* myself again, I'll make sure to have a Heinrichs nearby."

Mrs. Heinrichs is planning to patent her world-famous *fe'schlucke*-saving technique and is thinking of calling it the Heinrichs Maneuver.

Mennonite Woman Invites 4 People for Dinner but Cooks for 20

KITCHENER, ON

M rs. Louisa Bauman of Kitchener decided to invite the Erbs and Musselmans for dinner last night and since there was going to be a total of six people, she naturally decided to cook a meal for 20.

"And I don't mean 20 Englishers; I mean 20 Mennonites," said Bauman. "I want to make sure I've got enough to feed my hungry guests and about a dozen other people to boot."

Even though the couples were completely stuffed after the main course, Mrs. Bauman continued to bring out more food, piling it onto everyone's plates.

"I'll be devastated if you don't clean off your plates and ask for more," said Mrs. Bauman. "I'll consider it a great failure if you're not going home 30 to 40 pounds heavier."

After reaching a satisfactory weight, the two other couples waddled out of the Baumans' home and reached their parked cars, only with the assistance of Mr. Bauman, who prevented the over-stuffed couples from collapsing on the front lawn.

"Oh, those Erbs and Musselmans, they eat like mice!" said Mrs. Bauman, shaking her head in disgust. "Look at the situation they put me in. Now, what the dickens am I going to do with all these leftovers?"

WELTLIJCHTJEIT

(WORLDLINESS)

Toronto Riots After Discovering It's Not the Centre of Canada

TORONTO, ON

Toronto City Council held an emergency meeting this past week after a large "Centre of Canada" sign was erected on the highway near the small town of Landmark, Manitoba.

"What on earth is this?" asked mayor John Tory to a group of bewildered councillors. "This can't be for real, can it? The last time I checked, the centre of Canada was somewhere on Yonge Street, and certainly no farther west than Spadina!"

The news caused great concern for council members, who worried the city would be sent into a panic if this information was leaked to the public.

"Who do those Manitobans think they are?" said Tory. "Don't those folks realize the impact this sign will have on our fair city?"

Soon after the meeting, a rival councillor, seeking to discredit the mayor's leadership, posted a photo of the Manitoba sign on Twitter. The reaction was immediate, as millions of Torontonians took to the streets to express their rage.

"We haven't seen anything like this in Canada since the Vancouver Canucks lost in Game 7," said one news reporter. "I just hope this all calms down before someone gets hurt."

In an effort to pacify the angry mob, mayor Tory took to the airwaves.

"My fellow Torontonians, calm yourselves, please!" begged Tory. "Yes, it is true, Toronto is not the longitudinal centre of Canada, but I have no doubt in my mind that we still are, and always will be, the absolute centre of the Universe."

The words seemed to reassure city residents, most of whom quickly discarded their Molotov cocktails and returned home to watch the Maple Leafs lose yet again.

Single Snowflake Causes Vancouver Schools to Shut Down for 'Snow Day'

VANCOUVER, BC

The discovery of a single solitary snowflake in the Vancouver suburb of Burnaby this Monday forced schools across the region to shut down for the day. The sighting was reported early Monday morning and immediately caused a panic throughout the Lower Mainland.

"The kids are happy about it. They're all clamouring for space to go sledding on the snowflake," said Vancouver Public Safety Administrator I. M. Friesen. "However, it sure wreaked havoc on our infrastructure. We didn't budget for snow clearing this year."

The single snowflake was the largest winter storm of the season and, as a result of the wintry weather, traffic was backed up for miles on the 7A.

"The morning commute was horrible," said Friesen. "Vancouver drivers simply aren't used to these kinds of harsh driving conditions. It's a good thing they closed the schools."

Vancouver residents were quick to take selfies with the snowflake and post them on Facebook and Instagram.

"You know, we're not as fragile as everyone on the Prairies thinks we are," said Miss Zacharias, sporting a Canada Goose parka and clunky Sorel boots. "Just look at me handling this snowflake like a boss!"

In an effort to protect the city's reputation, the city of Vancouver will be offering free umbrellas and galoshes to all arrivals at YVR. Schools are hoping to reopen on Tuesday, so long as parents let their children walk to school in the frigid 7°C temperatures.

Hutterite Colony Selected as New Amazon Headquarters
RIDGE STREAM COLONY, AB

After months of meticulous research, Amazon has made its decision. The online shopping giant announced today that their new headquarters will be set up on a small Hutterite colony in southern Alberta. While many large cities across North America attempted to lure Amazon, in the end it was decided that the Ridge Stream Colony was the best fit.

"We're very excited. Currently we have about 120 people on the colony," said Mr. Franz Waldner, a Ridge Stream leader. "It will be quite the challenge to house and feed 50,000 more people, but if anyone's capable of doing it, it's us Hutterites."

Currently, the main industry on the colony is chicken farming, but Ridge Stream residents are looking forward to processing and shipping Harry Potter books and essential oil diffusers instead.

"The ladies are already working on making thousands of flower dresses for our new residents," said Waldner. "The communal seating at mealtime will be a bit of a challenge, but it's nothing we can't handle. We served just as many people at the Grand National Hutterite Softball tournament back in '93."

Amazon says they selected the colony because of the Hutterites' reputation for hard work, low labour cost, and wholesome farm-to-table cooking.

"Calgary and Toronto desperately wanted us to move there," said Amazon CEO Jeff Bezos, "but one taste of the famous Kleinsasser roast chicken was all we needed to make this decision."

The new 10-million-square-foot facility will be open at Ridge Stream Colony by early 2022 after which time all Amazon purchases will come with a copy of *The Complete Writings of Jakob Hutter* and a free German beer sausage.

Mennonite Child's Macaroni Art Purchased by the Louvre
PARIS, FRANCE

For the first time in its long history, the world's most prestigious art museum will include Mennonite macaroni art as part of its collection. Starting this fall, little Jessica Berg's *Self-Portrait in Macaroni and Rice* will be displayed alongside such masterworks as the *Mona Lisa* and the *Venus de Milo*.

"We're very excited to make this acquisition of macaroni art," said Louvre curator Marie Dubois. "Berg is a master of negative space and texture. She uses Elmer's glue to create a profound commentary on contemporary life."

Pastor Dan of South Blumenort Gospel Mennonite Bible Fellowship says this purchase was a long time coming.

"Mennonites have a centuries-old tradition of making art with macaroni, so it's nice to see we're finally getting some recognition on the international stage," said Pastor Dan. "This is exactly why we set aside between $40 and $60 every year to provide the Sunday school kids with macaroni and non-toxic white glue. I'm glad to see that investment is finally paying off!"

Young Jessica was excited to find out her art had received such attention overseas and says she already has a few ideas for future projects.

"Our teacher, Ms. Klassen, said next week we're cutting out pieces of old jeans and T-shirts to decorate a Raggedy Anne picture," said Jessica, who was uncertain about the biblical application of this particular art project. "She's even letting us use the grownup markers!"

In other news, South Blumenort Gospel Mennonite Bible Fellowship's children's choir has won the Pulitzer Prize for Music for their stirring performance of "I've Got the Joy, Joy, Joy, Joy, Down in My Heart."

Canada Geese Return Home Just to Shit All Over It
STEINBACH, MB

Millions of Canada geese, that beloved symbol of all that is good and decent in our fair country, have returned home this week to completely shit over absolutely everything.

"The purpose of these geese in our ecosystem," explained conservationist Lee Kliewer, "is to coat your windshield in a thick layer of shit. Also park benches and sidewalks."

Apparently, the geese see widespread defecation as an act of patriotism.

"It's just one way of giving back to the community," said head spokes-goose Gordon McGoose. "We're just here to spread a little love into your lives ... and onto your patios, golf courses, and children's sandboxes too."

McGoose says he is especially fond of the giant pond outside the Mennonite Heritage Village in Steinbach.

"We're hitting that place up hard this year," said McGoose. "Think of it as a heartfelt symbol of our generosity."

Canadians across the country will spend the next six months scraping goose crap off the bottoms of their shoes until the geese, Canada's most recognized and beloved ambassadors, leave for the United States and Mexico in the fall, where they plan to continue spreading their message of faith, hope, and charity all over people's front yards and swimming pools.

Frat Boys Disappointed With Visit to Intercourse, Pennsylvania

INTERCOURSE, PA

Dozens of lecherous Pennsylvania frat boys are upset and considering litigation after a visit to the small Amish town of Intercourse failed to match their expectations.

"I truly feel like we were misled," said Alpha Sigma Sigma president Blake Martin. "It's awful. For a town called Intercourse, there sure are a heck of a lot of cattle."

The fraternity had been planning the trip to Intercourse for months with the understanding that the town would provide exactly the sort of recreation that pathetic young men of their moral character desire. Instead, they spent the entire weekend canning beets and reciting scripture.

"The only thing the young women around here seem into are quilts, baked goods, and Bible studies," said Martin. "I didn't come all the way from Pittsburgh to spend my weekend reading through the Book of Psalms."

The fraternity plans to take the case all the way to the Supreme Court ... or at the very least the Better Business Bureau.

"We expect to be adequately compensated for our pain and suffering, and also for the gas we spent getting here," said Martin. "I'm certain any sensible judge will see things our way."

The town of Intercourse does not plan to contest the case but offered the frat boys a coupon for a complimentary sticky bun or glazed donut in exchange for the promise that they, and anyone else of their ilk, would never ever come back to the town again.

Local Quilting Ladies Accidentally Attend Metallica Concert
WINNIPEG, MB

The ladies from the Winkler EMMB Quilting Group were in the city this weekend to attend a panel discussion about the nine-patch block pattern at the Millennium Library, when a mix-up in the elevator and a journey down a series of confusing hallways led them to an arena filled with slovenly metal fans.

"Oh, *jauma*, this is certainly not what I was expecting," said veteran quilter Mrs. Brandt, 73. "Thousands of young men thrashing about in unwashed T-shirts and smelling worse than Onkel Jack after feeding the pigs!"

When the mix-up was discovered, Mrs. Brandt immediately demanded they quickly depart, but the other ladies were not convinced.

"We drove all this way from Vankla," said Mrs. Falk. "We might as well stick around for Kirk Hammett's solo on 'Ride the Lightning.'"

The other quilters agreed with Mrs. Falk and soon found themselves in a sweaty mosh pit in the middle of the crowd.

"*Oba*, I've never seen Mrs. Krahn crowd-surf like that before," said Mrs. Falk. "At church she's much more reserved."

After the concert, the ladies' ears rang as they drove home to Winkler and vowed never to tell their husbands what they really did in the big city.

Donald Trump Proposes Gigantic Wall to Keep Out the Mennonites

WASHINGTON, DC

In a recent interview with Fox News, Republican Presidential candidate Donald Trump suggested that the best way to solve America's problems is to build a giant wall to prevent the flow of Mennonites into the country.

"The Mennonites have got us surrounded," Trump said to a crowd of enthusiastic supporters. "They're in Mexico. They're in Canada. My first priority as your President will be to get a wall built to keep those strange Anabaptist folks out."

As peace-loving people, Mennonites have not been Trump's biggest supporters, and pundits have suggested this may be the reason he holds such animosity towards them.

"They're not like us," Trump said. "They dress funny, they eat strange food, and worst of all, they're pacifists. If there's one thing our country cannot tolerate, it's people who believe there are other ways of solving our problems than bombing the hell out of people we don't like."

When asked about the Mennonites who are already in the country, Trump said they would be "sent back to Mennovia or wherever they came from."

Hillary Clinton called Trump's remarks, "incredibly offensive," and said she had many Mennonite friends, but when asked she couldn't name a single one.

City of Abbotsford to Be Renamed 'Basically Vancouver'
BASICALLY VANCOUVER, BC

In a radical rebranding effort meant to accurately reflect the perceptions of outsiders, the city of Abbotsford, British Columbia, recently passed a motion to rename the community "Basically Vancouver."

"We also considered 'More-or-Less Vancouver' and 'Pretty Much Vancouver,' but eventually we settled on the name that most visitors were already calling it," explained mayor Heintje Brown. "We'd like to invite everyone to come explore Basically Vancouver this summer! You'll have a great time!"

Basically Vancouver gets thousands of visitors each year, especially from the Canadian Prairies, who love to tell friends back home that they drove all the way out to BC but didn't quite reach the coast.

"Oh, so you were in BC this summer? Did you get to Vancouver?" Mrs. Stoesz asked Mrs. Suderman.

"Yeah, well, basically."

The Sudermans spent three weeks visiting relatives out west, where they went strawberry picking at the Basically Vancouver Berry Farm and attended a foot-washing service at the Basically Vancouver MB Church.

"We had a great trip! It's a truly beautiful part of the country," said Mrs. Suderman, "though next year we're thinking of heading east and visiting Basically Toronto or maybe even Basically Montreal."

Upon hearing the news, the mayors of Kitchener, Ontario and Lachute, Quebec said they were eagerly anticipating the arrival of the Suderman family.

Mennonite Woman Wins Lifetime Achievement Oscar
LOS ANGELES, CA

Mennonite woman Deborah Kehler of Bergfeld, Manitoba was awarded the Lifetime Achievement Award at the Academy Awards last night for "more than 70 years of putting a smile on her face and pretending that everything is just fine."

"Mrs. Kehler is a remarkable actress," explained Academy spokesperson Susan Lawrence. "Whether it was a petty conflict at church about the time at which Sunday school should start, or the time her son went through a nasty divorce, or when her brother Pete was arrested for embezzling the town's rainy day fund, she was always there with a smile on her face and a few words of encouragement, even though deep down she knew it was all a bunch of crap. She makes Meryl Streep look like a beginner."

Kehler, who flew in from Bergfeld to pick up the prestigious honour, spoke to reporters at a press conference after the ceremony.

"This award is not just for me," said Kehler, hoisting her trophy in the air. "It's for all the amateur Mennonite actresses out there!"

Kehler, who recently underwent surgery after all those years of having to bite her tongue, says she was happy to accept the award, but is hoping she will be the last Mennonite woman to receive it.

"The Mennonite community should be more open to women expressing a full range of human emotions," said Kehler. "If you want to get angry, get angry. If you want to swear, swear. If you're feeling sad, don't tell people everything is okay."

Kehler then stormed out of the press conference, lit the trophy on fire, and yelled, "See, this is how it's done!"

Justin Trudeau Confuses Yerba Mate for Marijuana
NEW BOTWHELL, MB

On a recent visit to the small Mennonite village of New Bothwell, Canadian Prime Minister Justin Trudeau, who was elected last fall on a promise to legalize marijuana, mistook a yerba mate gourd offered to him by a Paraguayan man for something a little more illicit.

"Wow, thanks, man," the Prime Minister said as he slurped the tea through the bombilla. "Oh, sick, this is the good stuff!"

Yerba tea was brought to the Canadian Prairies by South American Mennonites who grew up drinking it in their home countries. Out of respect for their cultural traditions, the Prime Minister raised a cup of the loose-leaf tea in the air and promised to legalize and tax yerba in the very near future.

"If we control and regulate yerba, we can keep it out of the hands of children," Trudeau said, who by this point was shirtless and evidently feeling the effects. "Although I see some of you folks have already passed along the tradition to your young ones. That's okay. Who am I to judge?"

After witnessing the overwhelmingly positive response to yerba tea, Mennonites are now petitioning the Canadian government to also legalize rhubarb *plautz*.

Winnipeg Woman Spontaneously Combusts After Venturing Outside the Perimeter

WINNIPEG, MB

Marco Polo, Thor Heyerdahl, Amelia Earhart—these names are synonymous with exploration and adventure. Now we can add the name Alison Becker to the list, the daring Winnipeg woman whose recent journey to visit her friend Laura in Steinbach came to a tragic end, but not before she became the first Winnipegger ever to venture beyond the impenetrable Perimeter Highway that separates the capital city from the rest of the province.

Sadly for Becker, rumours about the misfortunes that befall anyone who visits the countryside came true as she vanished into a puff of smoke just as she passed the sign that says "You're only 25 minutes from Steinbach."

"She made it farther outside the city than any Winnipegger ever has," said her distraught husband, Ron. "I tried to convince her not to go. 'You don't know what's out there,' I told her. 'No one's ever left and made it back.' But going to Laura's Tupperware party was something she said she just had to do."

Becker trained for months leading up to the journey, first venturing out just a few metres, then a full kilometre, and eventually she was driving well past the A&W on the highway. With each trip she slowly increased her endurance and stamina.

"She was worried she might not have enough gas to make it back," Ron said of the epic 60-kilometre journey. "I insisted that she bring along a flare gun and a box of granola bars in case she got stranded. I guess those must have spontaneously combusted too."

Becker's accomplishment is being hailed by *National Geographic* as the "most significant achievement in exploration since Bartolomeu Dias reached the Cape of Good Hope in 1488," and has also settled the age-old debate about the reality of spontaneous combustion.

"If you ever wanted proof of spontaneous combustion, look no further," said Dr. Kelly Pearson of the Perimeter Highway Institute of Technology. "We can now pinpoint the precise cause of this phenomenon: visiting a friend in the country."

Since the tragedy, Becker has posthumously been awarded the Order of Manitoba for her "efforts in expanding the frontiers of knowledge about our vast and diverse province."

Meanwhile, huge signs have gone up warning folks about to exit the city that they are "entering at your own risk," though paranoid rural Manitobans have suggested the message could also face the other direction.

Schitt's Creek to Be Rebranded as *Schmidt's Creek* for Sensitive Southern Manitoba Market

TORONTO, ON

Emmy-winning and wildly popular Canadian sitcom *Schitt's Creek* will be rebranded *Schmidt's Creek* for the southern Manitoba market.

"*Oba, waut de hunt* is this yet!" said Mr. Klassen, adjusting his rabbit ears in disbelief. "A show called *Schiet Bach*? *Oba nä!*"

After just a few minutes of watching, however, Mr. Klassen was in stitches. He had to quickly change the channel and pretend to watch *100 Huntley Street* when his wife Lois walked in the room.

"*Diewel*! That was a close one!" said Mr. Klassen, the TV remote quivering in his hand. "Almost got caught watching something called *Schitt's Creek!*"

This problem of covert *Schitt's-Creek*-watching is so widespread in the region that television executives have decided to bowdlerize the show's name to suit the sensitive southern Manitoba audience.

"Our ratings were through the roof everywhere except the RM of Hanover and the Pembina Valley," said television executive Daniel Loewen. "We believe all it will take is a little tweak to the name and suddenly all the Penners and Reimers will be tuning in."

Schmidt's Creek will air Sundays at 5:00 p.m. ... just after *faspa* and before the evening service.

Sober Curler Discovered in Remote Manitoba Town
GLADSTONE, MB

The "Sober Curler" was long thought to be extinct in Western Canada, but scientists in Manitoba have recently confirmed the existence of one such creature in the small town of Gladstone.

"I've searched curling clubs across Canada. I've done thousands of breathalyzers … and everyone has failed. I've also done all the standard sobriety tests like the walk-and-turn and the one-leg stand, and not a single curler in all my years has ever passed," said Dr. Danielle Martens of West-Lake Polytechnic. "However, earlier this winter, I got a lead on the Gladstone Curling Club and I had to check it out."

Dr. Martens braved the icy roads and ventured out this past week to Gladstone where she found Mr. Ralph Koop, 51, in a state of complete sobriety.

"I couldn't believe it at first," said Martens, "but, sure enough, he passed all the tests. He hadn't touched a drop … and there he was sweeping and yelling 'hurry hard' and all that. It was truly marvelous."

The discovery of "Ralph the Sober Curler" is being hailed as a miracle across Canada. Ralph Koop has already undergone numerous laboratory tests to determine how all this is possible, but so far, the tests remain inconclusive.

"We don't know where he came from, or how he can curl without an ice-cold Molson in his hand," said Martens, "but we're just glad we found him. We're even hoping he'll mate with another curler and maybe produce some Sober Curler offspring."

A CBC history vignette about Koop is already in production.

Mennonite Biker Gangs Clash With Hells Angels at Sturgis
STURGIS, SD

South Dakota police were on high alert this weekend as dozens of horse-and-buggy Mennonite gangs, led by the notorious Swartzentrubers, descended on Sturgis for the annual motorcycle rally. Authorities were concerned that the introduction of more than 10,000 Mennonite and Amish buggies would not be well received by the more established biker gangs.

"I don't want horse shit all over my Harley tires!" said rival chapter leader Archie Harrison. "Let me tell you, this is our turf and if those Mennonites so much as open a hymnal around here there'll be hell to pay!"

The conservative Mennonites and Amish arrived in Sturgis on Friday, causing considerable confusion for the more than 800,000 leather-clad bikers gathered in town.

"I like the fact they wear black," said one biker, "but their women are a little over-dressed for Sturgis, and not a single one of them has a tattoo … that I can see, anyway."

Things got heated when Johan Yoder, one of the most high-ranking members of the Mennonite club, attempted to hold a solemn worship service in front of One-Eyed Jack's Saloon on Main Street.

The service lasted just two minutes before the Mennonites were completely surrounded by bikers who threatened to send them back to Pennsylvania on the next train out of town.

"We thought we were doomed," said Yoder, "but then quick-thinking Mrs. Yoder got out her collection of lovely pictorial quilts. The crowd went quiet. Moments later, however, a bidding frenzy began. Let me tell you, it was the best quilt auction we've ever had."

The Mennonites left Sturgis on Monday with fond

memories and a little bit of pocket change, while more than a thousand bikers left town with amazing handmade quilts they'll be sure to treasure for years to come.

Patrik Laine Traded to the Blumenort Menno Knights
BLUMENORT, MB

After months of speculation, the Winnipeg Jets have revealed that superstar Patrik Laine and his $7-million-a-year salary has been traded to the Blumenort Menno Knights of the Hanover-Taché Hockey League.

"Everyone thought for sure he'd be going to the Grunthal Red Wings," said local hockey commentator and radio personality Dave Anthony, "but Blumenort offered a first-round draft pick and a 10-percent-off coupon for the Penner rafter shop, so that was a deal no one would pass up."

Laine is really looking forward to lacing up for the Menno Knights, just as soon as a Plett or Penner floods their backyard and builds a rink this winter.

"I mean, he was already scoring 30 goals a season at the NHL level, so just imagine what he could do with that Kornelsen kid from Ridgewood feeding him passes," said Anthony. "I don't want to set unrealistic expectations, but I wouldn't be surprised at all if he gets 40 or even 50 goals this year."

The Blumenort Menno Knights struggled with a 31-53 regular season record last year but are really looking forward to the boost that a player of Laine's calibre can provide.

"We haven't had a player of this quality since the Reimers left town in '87," said Menno Knights coach Brian Penner. "If he can work on his defence and play-making ability, I think we'll really have a winner on our hands! He might even be able to play on our first line …"

It's not yet known how the Blumenort squad will be able to pay the $7 million salary, but the Blumenort Church Women's Auxiliary is already knitting scarves and baking ammonia cookies to help offset the cost.

Puerto Vallarta to Be Renamed 'Little Winkler'
PUERTO VALLARTA, MEXICO

After nearly two-thirds of the Winkler population vacated their homes and showed up on a charter flight to Puerto Vallarta this past week, the mayor of the Mexican resort town has decided to rename the city in their honour.

"Mennonites love our city. Cheap booze. Great beaches. And best of all you can sleep in on Sundays," said the city mayor. "In honour of all the Mennos who come here every year from Manitoba, we're renaming the city 'Little Winkler' or 'Winkler of the South,' if you prefer."

The Ungers scored a great deal for a week in Puerto Vallarta but were really disappointed to find the Warkentins in the room next door.

"And guess who was strutting his farmer's tan at the pool last night? Mr. Hoeppner!" said Mr. Unger. "This place is swarming with Winklerites!"

The problem has become so bad that the Ungers are thinking about going to Mazatlán next year instead.

"I hear there's a good contingency of Rosenorters there every year," said Mr. Unger. "That's okay. As long as I don't have to run into the Hieberts at the buffet line every evening."

There are so many Winklerites in Puerto Vallarta that the hotels have added Plautdietsch menus in their restaurants and de-alcoholized *cervezas* to their swim-up bars.

Efforts Intensify to Dislodge Fred Penner From Log
WINNIPEG, MB

Efforts to dislodge beloved children's entertainer Fred Penner from a log in an undisclosed location intensified on Saturday afternoon.

"For years he's gone in and out of that log without issue, but he got stuck a few days ago and now we've got a backlog of 150 colourful guests and puppets waiting to get through," said rescue coordinator Thomas Reimer. "The Word Bird is getting really antsy, let me tell you."

Despite the tense situation, Penner remains in good spirits and says he's baffled as to how he got himself in this position.

"I guess I put my elbow where my knee should have been or my shoulder where my foot should have been … I don't know," said Penner from deep inside the log. "Let me tell you, that's the very last time I try to go in feet first."

An international team has gathered around Penner, hoping to dislodge the man so he can get back to singing delightful tunes for Canadian families.

"We're pulling out all the stops. We've got excavators, chainsaws, anything we can think of," said Reimer, "and when we get hungry, we've got plenty of sandwiches, beautiful sandwiches."

It's not known how long Penner will remain in the log, although he's really hoping to be free in time to get home and check on the cat.

Pennsylvania Mennonites Demand Equal Treatment by *The Daily Bonnet*

BIRD-IN-HAND, PA

Thousands of Pennsylvania Mennonites petitioned *The Daily Bonnet* this week to be "more inclusive" of their particular idiosyncrasies that they claim are ripe for mockery.

"That website is far too Canadian!" yelled Mr. Reimer of Lancaster. "Plus, when *The Daily Bonnet* guy does write about us, he always gets our last names wrong!"

Mr. Reimer and Mr. Klassen, two fine, upstanding members of the Pennsylvania Dutch community, claim that their culture is chock-a-block full of stuff to mock.

"Hex signs. Conestoga wagons. Folk magic," said Mr. Reimer. "We even have beards without moustaches. If that Andrew Unger can't find a joke in there somewhere, I really question his satirical abilities."

Mr. Klassen's family has lived in Pennsylvania since the late 1600s and says it is about time somebody satirized them.

"We've got more comedic material here than you can shake a stick at," said Klassen, although he clarified that stick-shaking is against his religion. "We even named a town 'Intercourse.' We're basically writing the jokes for you."

After getting the surnames all wrong yet again, *The Daily Bonnet* was inundated with emails from angry Stoltzfuses and Beilers, who also pointed out that the website had, yet again, used a picture of the Amish and mislabeled it Mennonite.

NFL Team to Hold 'Conscientious Objector Appreciation Day'

PHILADELPHIA, PA

The Philadelphia Eagles will be honouring the nation's pacifist heroes this season by wearing a tiny image of Dirk Willems on their helmets and inviting Conscientious Objectors and other members of the historic Peace Churches to attend a special hour-long ceremony before a game this fall.

"We've set aside all the tickets in section 101 at Lincoln Financial Field for COs and their families," said Eagles representative Harry Graber. "A football game should be a place to solemnly reflect on how each of us can live more peaceful lives, but sadly, many folks come here just to witness a violent spectacle. Having the Hershbergers in attendance should really change that."

However, not everyone is all that keen on the idea.

"If there's one thing I know about professional football," said one Eagles fan, "it's that it's all about militarism, plain and simple. Well, militarism and beer."

In an effort to show that pacifism is not just passive, the team is also asking fans to bring gently used clothes to donate to the local MCC thrift store. Famed Eagles blogger Colin Timson supports the plan.

"Makes perfect sense to me. I've always said we should focus more on the game itself and less on the military," said Timson. "Plus, the Eagles have been playing like a bunch of pacifists for decades."

Doctor Shortage Finally Solved as Thousands of Medical Experts Appear Online

NORTH KILDONAN, MB

The doctor shortage in Manitoba has finally been solved as thousands of people in the province with internet access are now apparently fully fledged medical experts.

"Over the last few years, we've seen a surge in medical expertise, not just here in Manitoba, but around the globe," said Dr. Ida Nickel of the Manitoba College of Physicians. "You know, I think I might as well retire and let Onkel Ike or Taunte Eva or whoever take over. Based on their Facebook comments, I have no doubt they can handle things from here ..."

New doctors are being born every day, it seems, with simply the click of a mouse.

"It's a miracle, really," said Dr. Nickel. "I always thought it took many years of training to become a doctor, but I now know that any Tupperware seller or beer league curler can become a medical expert simply by watching a couple YouTube videos that confirm their biases."

The surge in doctors has meant that thousands of Manitobans on waiting lists can finally see a physician.

"Some guy named Dwayne, who's been a medical expert since about the middle of April, will be seeing patients in his single-car garage just off Henderson Highway beginning November 1st," explained Dr. Nickel. "Meanwhile, we've got three-quarters of a local country gospel quartet who will be conducting surgeries in the youth room at the EMBC church on Tuesday and Wednesday evenings. Vasectomies? Bunion surgery? You name it, they can do it. We've got Susan from the church library administering the anesthetics and a retired dairy farmer named Jake operating the MRI machine."

Dozens of southern Manitoba doctors have reportedly quit their jobs since everyone seems to no longer need their services.

Vancouver Blizzard Blamed on Visiting Relatives From Manitoba

VANCOUVER, BC

As Vancouver was blanketed with an unexpected snowfall this weekend, locals searched for some explanation for the mysterious weather and finally found their scapegoat: the *frindschauft* visiting from Manitoba.

"It's the Friesens!" exclaimed local woman Melissa Klassen, whose ancestors moved to British Columbia in 1983. "Anytime we get visitors from Gnadenthal this always happens!"

The Friesens are being asked to stay in southern Manitoba from now on and to keep the snow out there where it belongs.

"I'm sick and tired of these Manitoba Mennos coming here in winter and bringing their weather with them," said Klassen. "Friesens of the world, listen: you are just not welcome here. Not in winter, anyway."

Klassen is already drumming up interest in filing a class-action lawsuit against the visiting Friesens.

"I haven't owned a snow shovel my entire life and today, for the first time, I had to go out and buy one!" said Klassen. "I expect to be compensated!"

The Friesens say they are not the ones to blame, and besides, doesn't it always rain whenever those BC folks visit Manitoba?

Manitoba Family Still Smelling Strongly of Chlorine a Week After Grand Forks Visit

GRAND FORKS, ND

The Klippensteins of Gretna had a great time at the Come Hither Motor Hotel in Grand Forks last weekend, but are having trouble washing the smell of chlorine from their bodies nearly a week later.

"We spent a little too much time in the pool," said Mr. Klippenstein, wringing out his trunks. "Next time I'll just watch from the sidelines while the kids swim."

Mrs. Klippenstein, who didn't enter the pool once, but spent more than five straight hours in the hot tub with a bottle of New Zealand Sauvignon Blanc and a book about Corsica, also had a recognizable aroma the entire week.

"I went to work on Monday and all my co-workers were like, 'Oba, Nita, you must have been in Grand Forks,'" said Mrs. Klippenstein. "I tried to mask the smell with *roll kuchen* grease, but it was simply too powerful."

The Klippensteins are already planning another trip to the hotel in Grand Forks, although the adults are thinking about spending most of the time wandering through the mall and trying on clothes that don't smell like the Come Hither pool.

NASA Confirms the Existence of Mennonites on Other Planets

WASHINGTON, DC

In a press conference earlier this morning, NASA scientists answered a question that has plagued Anabaptists since the early days of the Reformation: "Are there Mennonites on other planets?" The answer, it seems, is a resounding "yes."

"We have strong evidence that points to not only life on distant planets, but also the existence of thriving Mennonite communities," said NASA spokesperson Loretta Rempel. "Our telescopes have revealed huge lakes of *schmaunt fat* on Earth-like planets outside the Milky Way, as well as clear images of lifeforms who appear to be baptizing adults."

The newly discovered planet, dubbed "Menno-69c," is some 2,700 light years from Earth and it is not yet known how the Mennonites got up there.

"Mennonites love to travel. One theory is that sometime after the Russian Revolution, a few fringe groups from the Molotschna Colony broke off and headed into outer space," said Rempel. "In their quest to flee from sin and the world, they must have felt that Paraguay or Mexico were simply not far enough away."

NASA has made attempts to contact the distant Mennonite colony; however, it is not known whether the group has access to communication technologies.

"We're trying to send digital probes," said Rempel, "but since they're Mennonites, we're doubtful they will have the necessary electronic devices to pick up the signals."

NASA claims it will spend upwards of $3 trillion to launch a horse and buggy into outer space sometime later this year. It is hoped that the rather primitive shuttle will reach the planet within 10 years, after which time they will overtake the colony and force them to abandon their way of life and learn English.

FREIWILLIGES

(THE TALK)

The True Story of *The Daily Bonnet*
(to the Best of My Recollection)

The first time I ever watched a baseball game on television I was holed up in a dirty highway motel somewhere in South Dakota and lying on a coin-operated vibrating bed that my parents would not let me and my brother use, we assumed, for reasons of frugality. We'd left Steinbach early in the morning and driven 12 straight hours to see faces carved in mountains and reptiles kept in inadequately small cages. By the time we arrived, it was late and raining so we ordered pizza and sat around in the dimly lit motel room watching baseball, which was the only thing on that wasn't *Who's the Boss*, a show the Unger boys were most definitely not allowed to watch. Instead, we watched Boggs, Rice, Buckner, and a pitcher named "Oil Can" Boyd. Funny names, we thought. We kept waiting for a Penner or Friesen to walk up to the plate and go down on strikes, but it never happened, and not because Penners and Friesens are such good hitters. Rather, I learned over the course of three hours of riveting 1980s baseball that people with surnames like Penner and Friesen are mysteriously absent from the Major Leagues altogether. Like the residents of remote Easter Island who, after centuries of isolation, thought they were the only people on Earth, I too had been under the false impression that the entire world was full of nothing but Penners and Friesens.

I can't say for certain, but I believe that evening in that South Dakota motel may have been the moment when I first became conscious of my own background, aware of my place within the micro-culture we call Russian Mennonite. On the long return drive to Manitoba, even the bleak, treeless landscape and the backs of all the signs for Wall

Drug could not keep me from thinking about this new revelation. Being a Penner or Friesen or Unger (with everything that goes along with it) was not normal, I thought, or at least not universal. Other people had other backgrounds, and with them, other experiences. I returned to Steinbach with an ever-increasing realization that our surnames, our food, our twice (or thrice) weekly church attendance, our utterances of "*na jo*" when we wanted to extract ourselves from a tedious conversation, and exclamations of "*jauma lied!*" when the pastor's daughter wore earrings to church were quirks, unique to these people and this place.

I didn't take notes of my accumulating cultural observations. I still don't. However, my ability to retain and recall details has undoubtedly helped me in my writing and also in *Trivial Pursuit* matches with my wife during the pandemic. In most other games, from chess to crokinole to *Super Mario Brothers*, she destroys me, but I do have an edge in any game that involves a vast reservoir of otherwise useless information. I'm particularly good with world capitals. Rwanda? Kigali. Uzbekistan? Tashkent. And so on. Or when someone tells me a childhood story about a terrible mishap with the cash-and-carry toilet, or the Sunday all the young people were forced to publicly confess the sin of swimming in jean shorts at the pits—I retain those stories too. Even though many of these peculiar episodes predate my own lifetime, in some sense, they have become part of my own narrative and identity, and have turned out to not be such useless information after all.

In my novel *Once Removed*, writer Timothy Heppner sits in the coffee shop above the gas station to observe the locals and take notes for his writing projects. I can't recall ever doing anything like this myself, though people sometimes assume that I do. Since I became known as "*The Daily Bonnet* guy" (aka the town pariah) some folks have become rather leery of me, as if I'm sitting there watching, waiting for someone to do or say something worthy of use in an article. But I'm not. Not consciously, anyway. Still, *The Daily Bonnet* is a work of observational humour, even if some of those observations are distant memories now. Thirty years after my motel-room epiphany, I've seen the Russian Mennonite culture fade, at least in Steinbach. Plautdietsch is rarely spoken here anymore. I suspect this is the case in many other Russian Mennonite communities. Because of this loss, there's a nostalgia for our once-common cultural quirks, which is part of what's made *The Daily Bonnet* successful. The articles—some of them, at least—remind people of their childhoods, of things like *tüte* and German hymn singing and rubber overshoes in the church lobby. That's one aspect of *The Daily Bonnet*.

Then there's the *spott*ing (pronounced "schputting") or irreverent jesting—something Mennonite children are told not to do. "Don't *spott*." I recall one such scolding accompanied my mock enthusiasm for singing the bass part in "Church in the Wildwood." There's just something irresistibly hilarious about repeating the word "come" over and over again while Taunte Lina warbles the melody. This is *spott*ing at its most primal and, perhaps, its most innocent, since I really had no intention of making a point or causing any trouble. It was instinctual, spontaneous humour, though it did not escape my attention that it made the adults squirm. Still, I really didn't know what I was doing. It was satire without intent.

My childhood was composed of many innocent moments like this. My father was an electrician turned pastor and my mother was a bookkeeper who also ran a day care in our home while my father was in seminary. Apart from the mild disrespecting of a few hymns, I stuck fairly close to the rules. There was, however, the time in elementary school when I listened to a Bruce Springsteen tape on a friend's Walkman while we hid behind the since-demolished muraled wall at Woodlawn School. My Sunday school teacher had given me the impression that listening to "Born in the USA" was something best to be avoided. It wasn't Twisted Sister, but in Steinbach even the Boss was a bit suspect. I didn't see what was so wrong with it. The rules seemed arbitrary. Where in the Bible did it say not to listen to Bruce Springsteen? And why were there only ever George Beverly Shea records at the local thrift store? What happened to all the albums with drums? These were solid questions for a young child, the sort of questions that, without satisfactory answers, lead to further *spott*ing. My sardonic edge sprouted like the vast sunflower fields of Altona.

I also grew up in a home where we talked about politics around the dinner table as frequently as faith and sports. We discussed the Meech Lake Accord and the Gulf War and NAFTA and I had opinions (echoed from my father, no doubt) about all these topics. I even wrote a childhood political treatise called "Political Views of a 12-Year-Old." These family discussions, coupled with the corrupting influence I received from clandestine viewings of David Letterman and *The Simpsons*, meant that soon I had taken up amateur political cartooning. My favourite target was Canadian Prime Minister Brian Mulroney, who was an acceptable subject since my parents were no fans of his by that time either. I filled a half-dozen Hilroy notebooks with these cartoons. By age 13, I was officially a satirist.

It wasn't long before Mulroney was replaced with Chrétien and, despite the satirical potential that lay before me, my interest waned. I wasn't a good artist. I stopped drawing the cartoons and it would be more than 20 years before I would formally write satire again.

There was never a premeditated plan on my part to create the Mennonite counterpart to *The Onion*, but in 2016 there was an explosion of satirical news websites and I took note, thinking perhaps this was something I could do too. The fact that this new online medium was primarily text-based with an accompanying photograph meant that I could revive my satirical instincts without the burden of, you know, having any artistic talent. All I needed was the appropriate topic.

The impetus came in the spring of 2016 when the Steinbach city council voted against yet another expenditure of some kind. Was it the library expansion? The construction of our still unbuilt Performing Arts Centre? It really doesn't matter at this point. Irked by the council's predictable penny-pinching, I wrote this article and posted it on my personal blog. Reading it now after five years, I'm pleasantly shocked at the sass.

Here it is, *The Daily Bonnet* Vol. 1 No. 1:

Steinbach City Council Approves Plan to Move Entire Population to Mennonite Heritage Village
STEINBACH, MB

Disregarding months of public consultation that suggested residents preferred to stay in the 21st century, council members of Manitoba's third largest city voted Tuesday to move the entire population to the local pioneer village.

"I was elected to support prudent fiscal management," said one local councillor. "What is more prudent than living in a sod hut?"

Mayor Chris Goertzen opposed the motion, noting that the federal government was ready to support communities like Steinbach with infrastructure projects that would enable it to stay in this century.

However, the councillor who introduced the bill stated that, "even with significant funding from other levels of government, a city our size just can't afford such extravagances as libraries, paved roads, and electricity."

Other members pointed to Steinbach's history of balanced budgets.

"Rather than saddle them with debt," one member said, "I'm committed to leaving my children and grandchildren the city of my great-great-great-great-grandparents."

Despite the mayor's disapproval, the motion to relocate was passed by a 5 to 2 vote. Residents will be asked to leave their homes as soon as the soil is suitable for *semlin* construction.

Much to my surprise, the article, if you'll excuse my use of a common pre-pandemic term, went "viral." Thousands read it. Up until this point, my non-satirical blog posts garnered a few dozen readers, usually less than a hundred, but overnight this article received thousands of clicks. I was surprised. It seemed that I had stumbled onto something: news-style satire about Mennonites. I figured if I could write one satirical article, I could probably write a few more, and that's when *The Daily Bonnet* really began. A few weeks later, I registered a domain name and set up a website with the help of my brother Colin, whose knowledge of computers far surpassed my own abilities to simply turn my aging desktop off and then back on again. I created a logo, which has since been upgraded, and wrote five articles, proofread by my wife, Erin. The website launched in May 2016 and I've published consistently every single day since then. In the past five years, I've written close to 2,400 articles.

At first, I was kind of uneasy about having my name associated with the website. I'm a fairly private person and I also didn't know how people would react to what I was writing. I'd read an article by Katie Funk Wiebe in *The Mennonite*

Encyclopedia that described how satire had been attempted but never found success in Mennonite periodicals. I had also seen how Miriam Toews's novels had divided my own community. I was concerned. The prevailing assumption was that Mennonites don't "get" satire. And remember, you're not supposed to *spott*. Thankfully, things have changed since Wiebe wrote her article on Mennonite humour in 1989, and now Mennonites do appreciate satire or, perhaps I should say, Mennonites are capable of appreciating satire. After all, Mennonites are not a monolith, neither culturally, ethnically, or theologically. Not everyone appreciates the *spott*ing, of course, and I did receive a few strongly worded emails in the beginning accusing me of spreading "lies," but for the most part the feedback has been positive and I assume that those who don't like it have moved on to other corners of the Internet with more cat videos.

Over time, I became more comfortable with being "*The Daily Bonnet* guy" and people, it seems, became less worried that I might be lurking around the corner watching them, notepad in hand. I've also learned a lot from *Daily Bonnet* readers who've pointed out Mennonite-isms I wasn't aware of myself. One running *Daily Bonnet* joke about Hymn 606 was not even on my radar until *Daily Bonnet* readers kept mentioning it in the comment section on Facebook. I grew up EMC and EMB and my mother's side was MB—we didn't have any Hymn 606. I've learned a lot, too, through conversations with Holdeman Mennonite and Hutterite friends, and even Swiss Mennonites with their unfamiliar surnames, which are still as exotic to me as those in the Boston Red Sox lineup of 1986. I've also gained a keen interest in my family and local history. My childhood friend Jeremy (not a Mennonite, although he married one) keeps asking me why Mennonites are so obsessed with other Mennonites, or at least why I am, in particular. I don't have a great answer other than that I think it stems from my search for identity and community. *The Daily Bonnet* is part of that process. Satire, by its very nature, is critical, but I think *The Daily Bonnet* is as much a celebration of Mennonite quirks as it is a critique. It's both.

After writing over 2,000 articles, choosing the best ones for this book was a difficult task. There were a few factors involved in the decision-making process. We considered the quality and popularity of an article, and tried to have a diverse range of topics without too much repetition. We probably don't need five Dutch Blitz articles in this collection, do we? Another factor was whether the article had stood the test of time. Some *Daily Bonnet* posts spoof news events that are quickly forgotten and may not be understood years or even just months later. I've also revised many of these articles and I can confidently say that *The Daily Bonnet* has never looked better. I hope you'll enjoy our selections and won't be disappointed too badly if, once again, your Uncle Henry or Aunt Martha are not mentioned.

—Andrew Unger
Manitoba, Canada
June 2021

But what will the people think?

The Treachery of the Bonnet

Armin Wiebe

To write satirical news stories in a time of deliberate fake news and rampant misinformation is a treacherous endeavour similar to riding a unicycle on a tightrope. If the satirist forges ahead safely with well-worn clichés and stereotypes, readers may chuckle warmly, but maintain that they're not like that anymore. If the pin is stuck into more sacrosanct balloons, the satirist may be accused of mockery and disrespect. If the satirical news story is so cleverly written that readers accept it as fact, the satirist may unleash uncontrollable forces. So as with riding a unicycle on a tightrope, balance is all. *The Daily Bonnet* yo-yos from *schmaunt fat* to church schisms to Snopes-worthy wishful thinking, tickling the gentle reader with *plautz* that *schmecks* before darting in like a prairie *mig* drawing blood only to be soothed again by *vereniki* smothered in rhubarb sauce, keeping the wheel firmly on the rope.

Andrew Unger is Speaking Through the Flower

Robert Zacharias

I imagine that for readers with just a passing understanding of Canada's Mennonite community—those who might be excused for imagining us to be a uniformly dour and humourless bunch—the initial shock and delight of *The Daily Bonnet* must come from the very idea of Mennonite satire itself. For readers who grew up playing the Mennonite Game, however, the delight comes from a shock of recognition—not only of whatever minor foible happens to be the subject of a given *Daily Bonnet* post, but also of the mock-earnest literalism adopted in the website's faux-news format. In detail and in tone, Unger positions himself squarely within his community, reveling in the telling eccentricities of a people he is only partially embarrassed to call his own. And in offering satire for rather than simply of the Mennonites, he extends an under-appreciated comic tradition in the pages of Mennonite literature, affirming the community even where his jokes are sharp enough to sting.

If it seems a little presumptuous to describe *The Daily Bonnet* as "literature," I would note that critics have long insisted that the purportedly "plain" writing that characterizes so much Mennonite writing is, indeed, a distinct literary style. In fact, literary critics sometimes use the Low German phrase *derche bloom räde*, or "speaking through the flower," to describe how this stylized plain speech has flourished in Russian Mennonite comedic writing as the type of deadpan literalism central to the warm satire of Arnold Dyck's beloved *Koop enn Bua* stories and Armin Wiebe's *The Salvation of Yasch Siemens*. Like Dyck and Wiebe, Unger often relies on an exasperated understatement to chasten and tease, even as individual posts on *The Daily Bonnet* occasionally lean into sarcasm (and so might be better described as *schputt*ing) or turn on a clever pun (and so are best thought of as *wuatspell*). The enthusiastic reception of the website among the very people it is ostensibly satirizing, however, suggests that Unger has earned his place in the community as another one of those *sposijch* Mennonites—you know, the *schriewa* who are always speaking through the flower.

On Ungerian Satire

nathan dueck

We talke of things which to our selves pertaine
Which not to know would be a sinfull staine.
Are men by riches or by virtue blest?
Of friendships ends is use or right the best?
Of good what is the nature, what excells?
—Horace, *Satires II.VI*
17th century translation by Sir John Beaumont

Aesop gave us fables. Horace gave us satires. Unger gives us ...

Well, Unger gave my *onkel* something to share on social media. I had no idea my dad's Big-Brother-is-watching-you big brother was even online until he tagged me in a comment below an article from *The Daily Bonnet*. It said something like "This Is Funny!" but I took it to mean "Why Can't You Write Something People Like?"

Funny is only part of *The Daily Bonnet*, though. Commentary's another part. Following the tradition of Horace's *Satires*, Unger teases readers to give us the chance to laugh ourselves free of folly. In the lines that follow the epigraph, Horace retells Aesop's fable about the country mouse and the city mouse. The moral is more or less the same as you remember from your children's reader: be grateful for what you have—also, beware of domesticated pets. Horace comments on ironies that are so common we barely see them. That's why I think Unger is Horatian. He'd ridicule country Mennonites for wanting what their cousins in the *staut* have while secretly judging their immorality. At the same time, he'd deride city Mennonites for openly judging their ignorant country *fada* while wanting to get away from it all.

Horace relates how satire, at its best, encourages

self-awareness. At its worst, I'm guessing, it urges self-consciousness. The former is a type of writing that would guide readers to see the limitations of their own behaviours and beliefs; the latter sort could lead readers to worry about how their shortcomings appear to others. It'd be easy for Unger to criticize politicians with Mennonite surnames or condemn churches with "Mennonite" in their titles. But his satire doesn't divide or cut down. It's not about pitting Mennonite brother against *brooda*. Instead, it somehow finds a way to bind us together. That's easier said than done, given that Mennonites love a good shunning, or—better yet—an ol' fashioned schism.

I say this because I'm the Mennonite *müss* who moved to the city to study (which is why I've had occasion to read Horace), as that lifestyle made sense to me. And most of my kinfolk choose to live in the *launt*, as that way of life makes sense to them. Until recently, we've agreed about what "making sense" means. Now, every time I'm about to unfriend my uncle for posting about how the government tracks us through vaccine microchips, I recall when he typed my name in a comment about *The Daily Bonnet*.

Unger gives us reasons to laugh at each other and, hopefully, excuses to talk to each other too.

WEADABUAK ENN SOO WIEDA

(WORD BOOK ETC.)

The Daily Bonnet Glossary

A glossary of mysterious words, phrases, abbreviations, and other things Englishers might find troublesome, whether reading them in this book or when stopping for gas in Winkler.

Amish: the first group ever to split from the Mennonites. Trendsetters in that regard only.

Anabaptist: literally, a "re-baptizer." Figuratively, a whole host of other things.

arbüs/rabüs: watermelon. Consumed with great enthusiasm by Russian Mennonites as soon as temperatures reach a sweltering 15°C.

Biebel: the Bible. The most important book for Mennonites, just above *Martyrs Mirror*, *The Complete Writings of Menno Simons*, and all the Danny Orlis books.

bliewe, sette, and so on: commands given to dogs and disobedient Bergmans.

borscht: a soup that is properly made with copious amounts of cabbage, not beets.

bossem: bosom. The part of a Mennonite somewhere above the ankles.

botta supp: soup made from butter. What rich Mennos eat when they're all out of margarine *supp*.

brommtopp: a drum with horse hair attached. Playing one is even more attractive than playing an electric guitar.

broodaschauft: a church meeting to determine who is getting excommunicated this week. If you weren't invited to the meeting, it's probably you.

büak/bok: book. What we used to read before we had computers.

Chicken Chef: a popular chain of casual-dining fried chicken restaurants predominantly in rural Manitoba and Saskatchewan. Where Mennonites go after church.

clops/klopps: hamburger patties. Served bunless as all meat should be.

CMC: Christian Mennonite Conference. The church formerly known as Chortitzer Mennonite Conference. The only Mennonite denomination to have successfully changed their name and kept the same initials.

CMU: depending on the context, refers either to Canadian Mennonite University or Commonwealth of Manitoba Ungers.

Conrad Grebel: an early Swiss Anabaptist leader. Also the name of a post-secondary institution in Waterloo, Ontario known for its prestigious ABBA Studies program.

Co-op: a place to buy *knackzoat* and/or gas. Also where to meet a spouse if the selection at church is not very promising.

credit union: a financial services establishment that conducts business exclusively in Plautdietsch.

dääjlijch: daily. The frequency with which *The Daily Bonnet* is published and which the luckiest of Mennonite couples partake in *meddachschlop*.

dankscheen: thank you. Something you say upon reception of all handknitted sweaters regardless of whether they fit or look good on you.

darp: a tiny village where everyone speaks Low German and will look at you funny.

dietja!: see *diewel*.

Dietschlaunt!: mild profanity, literally "Germany." You're feeding the hogs when your cousin Herman, who is a total *schwäa*, deliberately drops the bucket in such a way that it splashes up onto your slacks. While wiping the slop from your pants, you might exclaim "*Dietschlaunt!*" though nobody really knows why.

diewel!: mild profanity, literally "devil." You're from Paraguay, Mexico, or Abbotsford, and so aren't used to the cold Canadian winters. When you arrive at the Winnipeg airport and are escorted by your cousins back to the farm in Plum Coulee, you might exclaim, "*Diewel*, it's cold out there once!" and your cousins will just laugh and say, "You call this cold yet?"

Dirk Willems: an early Dutch Anabaptist martyr. The subject of Steinbach's only statue. (Sorry to disappoint, but the Miriam Toews one is not real … yet.)

ditsied: this side (the east side) of the Red River in Manitoba.

doages'berejcht: a report on daily happenings in the Mennonite community. This is slightly more extensive reportage than the ever-popular *Duecks'berejcht*, which is just a report on daily happenings within the Dueck household.

donna!: mild profanity, literally "thunder." You know it will get your mouth washed out with soap, but you're so upset over the fact that your brothers Henry, Hans, Kjnels, and Peter all got to go to the Ascension Day service, but you had to stay home and milk the cows, so you exclaim, "*Donna!*" and are immediately punished to the fullest extent of the law since it doesn't really mean "thunder" but actually means "Hell" and you should know better than to say such things.

düak: a kerchief or head covering worn in church by conservative Mennonite women and not just the Duecks.

Dutch Blitz: a fast-paced card game where players throw Amish-themed cards on the table all at once.

een: the number one. The amount, in dollars, that Mr. Warkentin tithes each week.

EMC: see *Kleine Gemeinde.*

EMMC: Evangelical Mennonite Mission Conference. EMC but with a bonus M.

EMMMC, CMMC, CMCMCC, MMB, EMMB, MEMC, MCMCMCC, etc: Mennonite denominations that do not yet exist but no doubt will after a few more church splits.

emm tjalla: in the basement. Usually referring to the old Eaton's store in downtown Winnipeg.

Enjelsch: people from England, or basically anyone who speaks English.

enn soo wieda: and so on. When calling the children in for dinner, Oma might yell, "Soup's on! Time to wash up, Jacob, Sarah, Anne, David, Elizabeth, Helen, Menno, Aganetha, Art, Abe, Klaas, Esther, Mary, *enn soo wieda.*"

fääsenja: the worship leader in church. Usually sings just a little bit out of tune.

faspa: a light lunch preceded by *meddachschlop* and succeeded by the evening service.

fe'schlucke: when food or beverage goes down the wrong tube. Apparently, this happens so often to Mennonites that we have a special word for it.

fleesch: meat. Literally every part of the animal.

flitzepee: bicycle. Considered sinful until 1994 when controversial Bishop Enns liberalized the Mennonite transportation laws. He permitted rollerblades at the same time.

foarmaworscht: farmer sausage. Normally made from pork, not farmers.

footjelentj: ankle. The most intimate part of a Mennonite's body.

freiwilliges: an open mic during a funeral when anyone can go up and lie about how well they knew the deceased.

frindschauft: a relative, often a Reimer.

fülenza: a lazy person. A person who doesn't farm.

General Conference: people who sing "Praise God from Whom All Blessings Flow" the wrong way. See MC (not EMC, EMMC, or MCC).

glums koki: small fried pancakes made of cottage cheese. Literally "cottage cheese cookies." Inspiration for the popular Mennonite children's TV character the *Glums Koki* Monster.

gnurpel: cartilage. Something to chew on while waiting for the pie to be served.

hinjarenj: backside. "Those wooden pews sure did a number on my *hinjarenj.*"

holubschi: cabbage rolls. Thankfully contains more meat than cabbage.

hungrijch: hungry. The feeling between church and *faspa.*

hunt: a dog. The word can also follow "*waut de*" to create a mild expression of disgust.

Hutterite: sort of like Mennonites, but much better at hockey.

jantsied: the other side (the west side) of the Red River.

jauma lied!: mild profanity, literally meaning "pitiful people!" Let's say that your cousins Frida and Elsie are sitting around the quilting circle and gossiping about the other cousins who are not present because they're probably off galivanting with the Neufeld boys. Frida might say, "*Jauma lied!*" to Elsie and Elsie would nod in agreement or perhaps say, "*Oba jo!*"

jeräd: to talk. Normally in Low German interspersed with a few words of English.

jo: yes. What you say when asked to clean up the chairs after *faspa* and what you definitely do not say when your Lutheran friends invite you over for a few pints.

jreen schaubel supp: green bean soup. Contains more sausage than beans. The author's favourite.

jreewe: cracklings. The healthiest and most delicious part of the pig.

kjielkje: short, thick noodles served with *schmaunt fat* when everyone's too tired to make *vereniki*.

kjnipsbrat: the sport of crokinole. A flicking game.

kjnipse: to flick. See *kjnipsbrat*.

Kleine Gemeinde: literally "small church." A denomination of Mennonites now known in Canada, at least, as Evangelical Mennonite Conference and headquartered in Steinbach. Founded by Andrew Unger's great-great-great-great-grandfather Klaas Reimer.

knackzoat: sunflower seeds. Used as a snack or to attract a prospective spouse.

komst borscht: a hearty soup with a perfect 10:1 farmer sausage to cabbage ratio.

küak/kok/koki: a cookie. May contain ammonia.

kubasa: kielbasa. A smoked garlic sausage from Eastern Europe. *Foarmaworscht's* main competitor.

lenj: thigh. Used only in reference to poultry.

Mennonite: nah, I ain't gonna touch this one.

Menno Simons: 16th century Anabaptist leader and founder of the Mennonites. Formerly a Catholic.

MB: Mennonite Brethren conference. They dunk, not pour.

MC: Mennonite Church. Not a rapper. See General Conference.

MCC: Mennonite Central Committee. A group known for a variety of philanthropic enterprises including, but not limited to, selling mixed and matched teacup and saucer sets at affordable prices.

meddachschlop: an afternoon "nap." Notice the quotes.

mensch ekj saj!: mild profanity, literally "man I say!" Suppose Onkel Henry has traipsed into the kitchen without taking off his barn clothes and has now soiled the freshly mopped floor with his dirty boots. Taunte Lise might say to him, "*Mensch ekj saj!*" and he would know he had done something really wrong and feel very remorseful.

nä: no. Pronounced "nay," this word should not be confused with *na*, which means 'well.' Of course, you can combine them in fun ways such as *na nä* or *nä na*.

na jo (dan): "well yes (then)." A signal to the person you're speaking with that this conversation is over.

na, jung/mejahl!: "well, young man/young woman." If a boy or girl does something very bad they might get taken behind the barn, but if they only did something mildly annoying that just deserves a firm scolding, or if the annoyed adult is not a parent, grandparent, uncle, aunt, or older sibling and doesn't have the proper authority to impose full discipline, they would be told, "*Na, jung!*" or "*Na, mejahl!*"

na oba lied ekj saj: a whole bunch of Plautdietsch words that indicate disgust.

na, taunte: "well, auntie." Let's say you're driving into town to pick up something at the Co-op and your mother spots an older woman walking across the street in a flower dress and socks with sandals and things are a little out of place and she doesn't look very put together, then your mother might comment, "*Na, taunte,*" even though it's not really her aunt.

niejoahschkuake: New Year's cookies. A fried donut served with icing sugar. Sadly served only one day a year.

oba jo/nä: "but yes/no." You're sitting there in a nice Mennonite restaurant, peacefully waiting for your *glums koki* to arrive. When they do, you exclaim, "*Oba jo!*" and high-five the waitress. When she tells you they're all out of pecan butter tarts you shake your head and say, "*Oba nä.*"

oma: grandmother; the one who feeds you.

onkel: uncle; the one who complains a lot about politics.

oola: old man. Commonly seen nursing a coffee all afternoon at A&W.

opa: grandfather; the one who tells you stories he claims are true but probably aren't.

päpanät: a tiny cookie with the taste of a ginger snap but the texture of a jawbreaker.

Papsi: a dark sugary beverage consumed with Ravels.

paska: a sweet lemon-flavoured bread or bun with a cream-cheese-based icing and sprinkles. Served at Easter after all the *schintjefleesch* is gone.

Pennsylvania Dutch: a group of people not all of whom are Mennonite, and not all of whom reside in Pennsylvania, and none of whom are Dutch. Also the language they speak, which is also not Dutch.

perishky: a bun with meat in it of unknown specificity.

Plautdietsch: the Mennonite dialect of Low German. Commonly believed to be the language Jesus spoke.

plautz: a dessert. Also a currency in the MB church lobby after the service.

plümemoos: a cold plum soup, usually served as punishment when the grandkids are out of line.

poontje: pony. Any horse too young to pull a buggy full of Mennonites.

prachtvoll: gorgeous. A descriptive term normally reserved for sunsets and tractors.

Quaker: a like-minded Protestant denomination having little to nothing to do with oats.

rapple chaps: ripple chips. Old Dutch, preferably.

Ravel: a chocolate ice cream bar that just tastes better in Plautdietsch.

roll kuchen: a fried piece of dough, eaten with Rogers Golden Syrup and watermelon during long, warm Canadian summers (i.e., July).

ruehrei: scrambled eggs but with flour. Should be more doughy than eggy if you're doing it right.

Russian Mennonites: a group of Mennonites, few, if any, of whom reside in Russia and none of whom are Russian.

rüt met die!: literally "out with you." Oma Toews is still busy preparing *faspa* and has not cut the cheese yet, but the grandchildren are coming up from the basement already and have demonstrated themselves to have ants in their pants. Oma would then yell, *"Rüt met die!"* to the children and the children would go outside and throw rocks at the cows until it's time for *faspa*.

saengerfest: a festival of song singing with plenty of vibrato from Mrs. Jansen.

schekjbenjel: a gofer. A young, inexperienced worker who holds the ladder for you. Not usually suitable marriage material.

schiet bach: shit creek. A neologism for Mennonites, but one that really should've been in our repertoire much sooner.

schintjefleesch: ham. The part of the pig that rich Mennonites eat.

schlop: to sleep at any time, not necessarily *meddach*.

schmaunt fat: a white cream gravy, as essential for a Mennonite's survival as air and water.

schnetje: biscuits. Better than scones.

schuppse: to shove or pry. The method used to get cousin Andreas baptized.

schwaä: an insult meaning "festering boil." Cousin Herman is constantly causing trouble. Oma knows it. Opa knows it. All the other cousins find him such a nuisance yet. Behind his back, everyone says of him, "*Oba*, that Herman is such a *schwaä!*"

schwiena'rie!: an expression of disgust, but literally "a place where pigs are kept." You've been playing *kjnipsbrat* and Dutch Blitz all afternoon and Oma Koop doesn't like the sight of the *kjnips*ers and cards strewn all over her shag carpet, so she says "*Schwiena'rie!*" and you know it's time to clean up before she gets out the wooden spoon.

seea: very. As in "*seea* saxy" or "*seea* long sermon."

semlin: a temporary sod hut built by Russian Mennonite pioneers. Now selling for at least half a million in the hot Abbotsford real estate market.

sette: see *bliewe*.

somma borscht: a *borscht* variant containing sorrel that is served in summer or by heathens in winter.

spezeare: to gossip over coffee about the Klassens in the church lobby.

spott (schputt): sarcasm, mockery. *The Daily Bonnet*.

Stille Nacht, heilige Nacht: a popular song sung at Christmas, normally in English with an extra verse in the original German to please Oma.

Swiss Mennonite: the sort of Mennonites with weird last names.

taunte: aunt. May also be used for any older woman wearing brown nylons.

tjäatjsche: a kitchen maid. Usually marries a *schekjbenjel*.

tjinja: children. Usually come in quantities of 12 or more.

tjnette: to knit. How clothes are made.

trajchtmoaka: an untrained folk "chiropractor" who accepts payment in chickens or trays of *plautz*.

truärijch: sad and/or pathetic. "Andrew Unger's attempt at writing a Plautdietsch dictionary was completely *truärijch*."

tüte: brown paper bags filled with peanuts, gum, and gospel tracts, given to Mennonite children at Christmas. What every Mennonite child gets instead of the Nintendo they wanted.

Vanapag: how Mennonites say Winnipeg.

Vankla: how Mennonites say Winkler. Aka *jantsied*.

vereniki: a dumpling filled with cottage cheese, covered in *schmaunt fat* (sour cream not permitted), and eaten in quantities of 10 or more at a time.

waut de schissjat?: mild profanity. The closest thing we get to "what the heck?" Church is about to start and Justina Epp is still standing on the men's side talking to Abe Peters, and so you whisper to her, "*Waut de schissjat*, Justina, get over here!" and she quickly scampers over to the women's side and everything is much better after that.

waut es met die?: "what is with you?" An expression usually bestowed on Reimers.

weadabuak: word book. A place to disregard everything else and just look for the swears.

weltlijchtjeit: worldliness. Includes owning a pool table, playing hockey on a Sunday, and listening to Amy Grant post-1990.

wolljack: a sweater knitted with love by a Mennonite *oma*. The sweaters knitted without love are called Walmartjacke.

Wunda Frü: Wonder Woman. Aka Mrs. Gerbrandt of Rosenort.

yerba tea (yerba mate): brought to Canada by Mennonites from Paraguay, this is a thick green tea served cold or hot and drunk from a bull's horn through a metal straw. Often mistaken for cannabis.

zwieback: a bun with another small, superfluous bun on top.

Dankscheen

I'd like to thank the amazing folks at Turnstone Press, especially Sarah Ens and Melissa Morrow, who worked directly with me in the editing process. Thanks also to my wife, Erin, who is the person on whom I most often try out my new material. Thank you to all *The Daily Bonnet* fans for reading my work over the years, for not getting (too) angry, and for proving that despite our dour reputation, Mennonites do indeed have a sense of humour.

—Andrew Unger